# Shrugging Off the Wind

## Tall Tales from Easington Writers

edited by

Wendy Robertson and Avril Joy

Designed and produced by **hpm**group  Tel 0191 3006941

ISBN 978-0-9564823-0-3

# Contents

# Foreword

Three years ago Easington Writers was set up by Mary Bell in response to interest shown by local writers. It has developed into a springboard for burgeoning writing talent in the Easington District. Now we have a strong group of people, some of whom have written for years, some of whom are newcomers.

In 2007, supported by Easington District Arts Officers we made a successful bid for National Lottery funding for this Tall Tales Project. In our bid we emphasised that we would use our writing skills to tell stories emerging from our conversations in the community with such groups as Ladies' Club, Donnini House, Rutherford House and Robinson House as well as with individuals of Easington and Horden.

The people in these groups have shared stories of their lives with us and inspired our fiction. In addition to this input, our own lives here in the Easington district, fortified by our own imagination, have generated these fictional stories and poems.

This very special book *Shrugging off The Wind* fulfills our original vision of making our writing widely available in book form. Now people from Easington and the wider world can read and enjoy at leisure this book which will be launched by a reading event which will, we hope, encourage others to take the plunge and be inspired to write.

The Tall Tales Project has been based on a series of very challenging workshops by project director Wendy Robertson supported by writer Avril Joy and writer/publisher Gillian Wales, who have ensured our involvement in the whole writing and publication process. It has been a privilege and an outstanding opportunity for us to work with Wendy and Avril. We've had ten wonderful workshops and have been taught to an exceptional level all about creative writing. Saying thank you is not enough for these three special people who have taught us so much - how to harness our knowledge and inspiration to write creatively, how to develop our writing skills, how to edit our own work, and to tackle poetry written in the modern style. The process has been like taking rough stones and turning them into gems. The sea glass found among the pebbles in this corner of the North East now has a luminosity that wasn't there before.

Most of all, they have shared their lives with us and encouraged us to see ourselves - like them - as writers. They have made a dream come true for Easington Writers.

Mary N. Bell
Susan Robinson
For Easington Writers

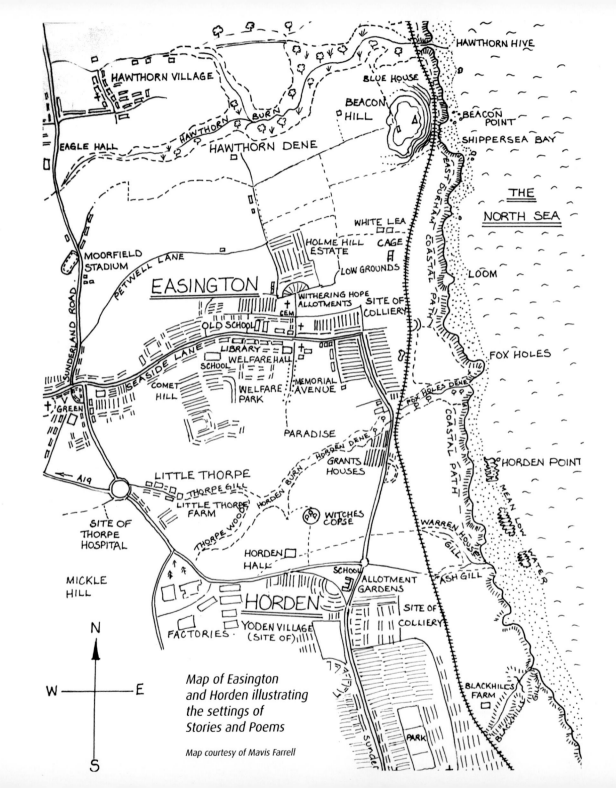

HAWTHORN HIVE

HAWTHORN VILLAGE

BLUE HOUSE

BEACON HILL

BEACON POINT

SHIPPERSEA BAY

EAGLE HALL

HAWTHORN BURN

HAWTHORN DENE

THE
NORTH SEA

WHITE LEA

CAGE

EAST DURHAM COASTAL PATH

MOORFIELD STADIUM

PETWELL LANE

HOLME HILL ESTATE

LOW GROUNDS

LOOM

EASINGTON

WITHERING HOPE ALLOTMENTS

CEM

SITE OF COLLIERY

SUNDERLAND ROAD

OLD SCHOOL

FOX HOLES

LIBRARY

WELFARE HALL

SEASIDE LANE

SCHOOL

COMET HILL

WELFARE PARK

MEMORIAL AVENUE

FOX HOLES DENE

COASTAL PATH

GREEN

PARADISE

HORDEN DENE

HORDEN POINT

LITTLE THORPE

GRANTS HOUSES

A19

THORPE GILL

LITTLE THORPE FARM

HORDEN BURN

MEAN LOW WATER

SITE OF THORPE HOSPITAL

THORPE WOOD

WITCHES COPSE

WARREN HOUSE GILL

MICKLE HILL

HORDEN HALL

SCHOOL

ALLOTMENT GARDENS

ASH GILL

FACTORIES

YODEN VILLAGE (SITE OF)

HORDEN

SITE OF COLLIERY

BLACKHILLS FARM

PARK

BLACKHILLS

N
W        E
S

*Map of Easington
and Horden illustrating
the settings of
Stories and Poems*

*Map courtesy of Mavis Farrell*

# Preface

When we agreed with the Easington Writers' group to mentor and tutor them through their Tall Tales Project, we did not realise what we were getting into. First there was Easington itself. We knew of its strong association with the history of mining, right up to its crucial involvement in the 1984 Miners' Strike. We also knew that – in common with most mining districts – it had lost its mines and with that its central livelihood and its working energy.

But, until we went there regularly to work with the Easington Writers' Group in their magisterial Welfare building, we had not realised the beauty of this place, with its long beaches and inlets, its wooded denes and everywhere the sea. Of course now there are no gantries and pit wheels but – as at least one poem here shows – these icons of a bygone age are missed and are still seen to have had their own unique beauty.

The other special delight has been the sheer character, energy and originality of the writers with whom we have worked. As these very original writers tackled our writing tasks with open minds, the quality of their writing grew enormously, month by month. They have embraced the challenge of transforming fact into fiction with great imagination and have written pieces which contain gold nuggets of truth for all of us, whether or not we come from Easington.

These writers, having fulfilled their brief to talk with Easington people, have come back with stories ranging widely from well-researched historical tales, to tales of Easington before even the railways arrived, to heart-felt narratives based on Easington's mining heritage, to contemporary tales of the disaffection of the young and the social consequences of the lost industrial base. Here also are well-wrought ghost stories and poems of lyrical quality that reflect the poignant beauty of the landscape and its meaning for Easington people. Humour and occasional roguish insight lace many of the stories with the unique quality of the Easington point of view.

**Wendy Robertson and Avril Joy**
Easington Tall Tales Project

# We're Not Dead Yet

Terry Dobson

Empty houses boarded windows
Sightless lifeless piles of brick
No whistling chattering booted feet
Of men heading for their shift

Community spirit battered, shattered
Shops closed shutters down
Standing vacant still and hoping
For better times to fill their shelves

Shrugging off the North Sea wind
We're made strong hewn from rock
Like the shafts sunk down below
Proud that we're from mining stock

Children running, laughing, singing
Playing ball and walking dogs
Marching onward to the future
Heads held high, no lowered eyes

So listen up, don't put us down
Don't count us out we're on our feet,
We keep on moving looking forward
To the future, we're not dead yet.

# Jimmy Cagney Was My Hero

## Susan Robinson

Jack Maratty stands on the cobbles of Third Street, Horden. His face scowls and his lower lip juts into the scream of words that surround him.

'Your dad's not your dad,' they yell.

He swallows, his throat tight. His heart thuds in his chest while his hands form into fists. They tense and strain, tighter and tighter until his fingernails dig deep into his palms. Then he reaches down and picks up a sharp stone from the road. He gestures wildly; his right arm waves above his head as he circles around looking for the ringleader. It's Billy Spence. He aims. They scatter.

'You're a bastard, and all.' The thin echo of the small child's voice seems to hit him in the belly. He feels winded. He breathes hard and fast and, realising that he is standing all alone, he drops the stone and begins to run.

Jack is twelve, a skinny kid with floppy fair hair. He has a scar from a scald that happened when he was three. It covers half his face. He thinks it makes him look like a gangster. His hero is Jimmy Cagney. That's who he'd like to be.

Jack is tough. He can cope with the other kids in the street, no bother. Why only yesterday he'd punched Billy Spence just for looking at him the wrong way. But they'd ganged up on him today. Five to one against. The odds were not in his favour. They might have called him a bastard before, but he'd never heard them say that about him and his dad. He was baffled. He'd sort that Billy Spence out the next time he saw him.

But for now, it is Saturday afternoon, and the matinee at The Picture House will be starting soon. Jimmy Cagney in 'The Public Enemy'. He can't wait. He's seen it twice already. He gets to his house and barges in through the back door. 'I want some money for the pictures, Mam,' he shouts. 'Mam, are you there, did you hear me? Mam?'

His mother appears at the scullery door with a shilling in her outstretched palm. 'Here you are, son. Off you go. Enjoy yourself.' Nothing's too good for their Jack.

It's only twopence to get into the pictures - well in the dog-end that is. He'll keep the change to buy some Woodbines. He knows his mother spoils him. Most would say 'spoils him rotten'. He turns to go, but on second thoughts turns back. 'Am I a bastard, mam?'

'Aye,' she says.

He holds his breath. She seems to look at him for a long time.

'Aye, you are, sometimes anyway.' She cuffs the air around his head, her hand falls to ruffle his hair. 'Get yourself off to the pictures now; you're going to be late.'

For two hours Jack loses himself in gangster land. He comes out of the picture house darkness with a swagger to his step and a curl to his lip. He bumps straight into Billy Spence. Jack, aka Jimmy Cagney, is on the ball. His right hand shoots out and grips the neck of Billy's jumper and hauls him against a wall. 'Billy Spence, we've got business to settle.'

'Aw, Jack!' Billy's pasty face grows paler.

'Not so clever now Billy, are you, without the rest of your gang?' Jack drawls out of the corner of his mouth. 'You've got this coming.' And he pushes his hand into Billy's face, squashing his nose just like Cagney would. 'If you don't want to be slapped about and your teeth knocked out one at a time, you'd better tell me what you meant about my dad not being my dad.'

Billy's face takes on a sickly grey tinge. He tries to swallow but instead snot spurts from his nose and tears gush from his eyes.

Jack releases him to wipe his hand.

Billy takes his chance and ducks away. He runs and shouts. 'You don't know, do you? You were given away, man. Nobody wanted you.' With that he's off, as fast as his ten year old legs will carry him.

For the second time that day Jack feels as if he's been punched in the gut. He closes his eyes, and tries to still the pounding in his chest. He feels sick and then dizzy. He opens his eyes and looks around. Nothing's changed. But everything has.

Back home, nobody's in. He helps himself to one of his dad's cigarettes. He won't know, he thinks, he can't count. His dad won't remember how many he had. And Jack needs a smoke right now. He needs something to make him less twitchy. He can't get his head around what's happened that day. He catches sight of himself in the mirror above the fireplace. His thin face looks back at him. It's the face he's always had. One that Jack had always thought looked like his dad's. Jack blows the cigarette smoke, trying for a smoke ring, trying to look hard and mean, trying hard not to let a sign of the tension he was feeling show. What had Billy Spence meant? Given away? Nobody wanting him? But he'd always lived here, with his mam and dad, hadn't he? And they'd always wanted him, hadn't they?

The scullery door opens and Jack's dad, John Maratty, stands in its frame. He is a rough hewn man with a gaunt face, blind in one eye and missing two fingers on his right hand from an explosion down the pit. Blackened from his day's work, he doesn't step beyond the threshold. He knows his place, and there'll be hell let loose if he dirties the front room with the filth from the mine. Kind by nature and put upon by wife and son, he digs in his pocket. 'Here, Jack,' he says, giving him some money. 'Fetch us some beer, will you, while I have my wash?' And he does as he usually does and goes into the backyard to bring the tin bath off the yard wall into the scullery.

Jack grabs the ladle can for the beer and then he scarpers. He doesn't wait to help with the water; it's heavy work. As he goes he hears his dad whistling his favourite tune, 'I'm forever blowing bubbles'. Jack knows it from the Jimmy Cagney picture he'd seen earlier. He imitates his hero now as he squares his shoulders, fingers an imaginary gun, slits his eyes and with a hard look to his face says out loud to a pretend Billy Spence, 'Why, you dirty, no-good, yellow-bellied stool. You ain't so smart, see. Nobody asked you to put your two-cents in. You got this coming. Bang, bang, bang.'

That felt better.

At the Nimmo's pub Jack gets the can filled with the warm, malty bitter that his dad likes. On the way back he does what he always does and has a few swigs. It's only half full when he gives it to his dad. The beer gives strength to his belly and a purpose to his tongue. He blurts out, without thinking too long about doing it or he'd chicken out. 'Dad, are you my real dad?'

John Maratty is quiet. There's a softness in his good eye. He breathes deeply. His thin lips disappear in a tight line on his face, like he's trying to keep in the words that he has to say from coming out.

Jack sees the hesitation, and feels scared. But he's tough, remember. 'It's all right dad, you can level with me. I can take it on the chin.' He stands in front of his dad, brash and cocky, a hard-boiled character but his insides churn in case his dad says the words he doesn't want to hear.

'No, lad, I'm not.'

At first Jack doesn't know what to say, or to do. He just stands there looking at his dad. He won't cry; crying is for girls. What would Cagney do? His lip begins to quiver, but he forces it into a sneer. 'So, I'm a real bastard, eh? I sort of figured I was different.' He shrugs his shoulders. But he drops his head so his dad can't see his wet eyes. He turns away.

'Wait,' says his dad. 'You need to know the rest.'

Aye, there was that STUFF about being given away and nobody wanting him. He wipes his eyes quickly on his jumper sleeve. He turns back. In his mind's eye he adjusts an imaginary trilby, pushing it back up on his forehead. He holds an imaginary machine gun ready. He's back in control now. He looks at his dad suspiciously. He waits.

'You should have been told before now. But your mam said no. Your dad, your real dad buggered off. Your *real* mam had gotten herself pregnant and he didn't want to know.'

'My real mam, what do you mean, my real mam?' Jack could hardly swallow. His tongue seemed like an old sock in his mouth. His head hurt, and his heart raced. He could hear Cagney's voice shouting "dirty double-crossing ....."

'Mam's not your real mam. Your real mam had it hard; she had no husband. She had to go out to work. At first she left you with us during the day, for us to look after you while she worked. We'd no bairns of our own, see......'

'So she didn't want me and she gave me away, huh?' That's why Billy Spence was pointing the finger.

'It wasn't like that. She cared for you. She looked after you when she didn't work. But then she married a man who didn't want you around. And you were used to us, and we wanted you. So you just stayed here with us – with me and your mam.'

The machine gun is firing off in his head. Cagney screams "you dirty rat" and sprays bullets in all directions. A single question ricochets like live ammo in Jack's brain. How does Billy Spence know this? 'What's her name?'

His dad shakes his head slightly, and then sinks his chin to his chest. 'Your real mam's name is Alice Spence.' The words are muffled but Jack still hears them. His dad raises his head. Jack holds his dad's gaze for what seems a long time.

Jack takes the stairs two at a time. He throws himself across the old iron bed he sleeps in. This is all he knows. This is his life. It has been for twelve years. He goes to school, and plays the nick, has his mates, plays football, goes to the pictures, steals a fag, swigs his dad's beer, has plenty of money off his mam, has fish suppers when other kids have nothing, even manages to put a bet on the horses with his dad's weekly gamble. This is him. Jack Maratty. But he isn't him anymore. At the moment he isn't even Jimmy Cagney. He is Billy Spence's half brother. And who the hell is *he*?

He wakes, still in his clothes, still lying across the bed. Darkness fills the corners of the room and in his head he can hear the faint sound of someone crying. He thinks it's him. Jimmy Cagney is whispering "you ain't so tough", so maybe it was him.

13

# Red Primroses

## Mavis Farrell

The roe deer trotted, still dainty, from Eagle Hall eastward towards the sea. She followed the course of the beck - passing the old mill race - deeper into the ravine. Her hooves made delicate slots in the soft earth of Hawthorn Dene. Sunlight filtered through the pale new leaves of spring, illuminating the white wood-anemones, making them shine like fallen stars on the woodland floor.

A spasm tensed her swollen belly, slowing her progress. Instinct was driving her to find a safe place where she would be hidden from the prying eyes of man, and from the dogs which sometimes raised their noses in the air and slavered in anticipation at the scent of deer.

The deer remembered a secret place where the hawthorns grew thick and tangled, where her scent would not betray her if she crossed and re-crossed the waters of the beck on the way.

At the meeting of the streams she entered the beech wood which was too open for safety but she had to cross it to reach the special place. She was stilled by another gripping spasm that tensed her body and was forced to rest a while.

Then she smelled *man*. The beech trees overhead rustled their warning but the deer heard only the metallic click as the hammers cocked. Gunshot shattered the silence, repeating itself again and again and again as it echoed the length and depth of the Dene.

The roe deer crumpled to the earth and would hear no more.

The pleasure on the face of the hunter soon turned to anger when he saw where the deer had fallen. The old beech tree stood on the edge of a gorge, its massive roots splitting the limestone rocks sculpted by ice ages. The impact had blasted her into a deep cleft where she lay guarded, out of reach of the hunter who was cheated of his prey.

Old Jimmy heard the shot as he made his way through the Dene to gather leaf-mould for his garden. The hunter crashed through the undergrowth towards him and he shuddered involuntarily, feeling the evil in the air. His sharp old eyes glimpsing the tattoo of a serpent on the back of the hand clenching the stock of the gun.

The Dene was filled with shock and silence. No bird sang. Bluebells bent to the earth. Primroses were stained red. There was a smell of sadness and death. The wind, gentle at first, blew last years' leaves into the cleft, between the roots of the beech tree, covering the deer and her unborn fawn.

The wind gathered up its strength. It howled with an angry intensity from the west to the east, raging the full length of the Dene, racing and rattling the white bones of dead elm trees in its path, destroying the fresh new leaves of the living trees, and raging down to Hawthorn Hythe where it made a maelstrom of the sea.

Night stole the day. Thunder rolled the skies. Lightening split the heavens, striking the beech tree and severing a limb which did not fall but instead, hung suspended, held only by smaller branches.

The wood waited.

Throughout the long summer and into the decay of autumn, the mental camera of the hunter's mind constantly clicks and snaps the roe deer falling. He knows no peace and is drawn back to the Dene, time and time again, where the wraith of a deer prances and dances ahead of him, along paths old and paths new but always out of reach and out of range and always ending its dance beneath the old beech tree. *Click snap, click snap, click snap.* The camera of his mind torments him until madness consumes him.

With the wraith in his sights he squeezes the trigger. The first shot shakes the woodland, dislodging the severed limb of the beech tree suspended overhead. As the branch falls the hunter drops the gun which bounces to the ground and on impact fires into his own face.

Now the silence was absolute. No bird sang. No breeze stirred the canopy. No lap-slap of waves on the pebbled beach. Crushed garlic scented the air with its pungent smell and a ghost of acrid gun smoke hovered, haunting the stillness.

The hunter lay, spread like a starfish, his face destroyed. Blood trickled from the remains of his mouth, spurting occasionally as the branch of the beech tree crushed his chest further into the soft earth. On the back of his hand the blue serpent writhed as his trigger finger tightened then relaxed. It was the last movement he would ever make.

Old Jimmy, on his daily pilgrimage through the Dene, found the body and without any sadness, notified those in authority. The body was eventually taken away.

The woodland soon recovered, reverting to it's previous tranquillity. The breeze shush-shushed gently, soothing the trees.

Today, if you were to walk the paths of Hawthorn Dene, you would see a huge scarred beech tree with a rotting branch lying beneath it. You may notice fungating, fly agaric decaying beneath the fallen branch. When you walk there in Spring you will be enchanted to see, growing under the bole of the beech tree, a very unusual patch of red primroses.

*Inspiration for this story comes from Hawthorn Dene itself, an ancient beech tree, the Roe Deer who live there, and the recent sighting of a man with a gun .*

# Passing Phantoms

## Agnes Frain

Enclosing bricks soot encrusted beyond conservation
Rough muddy pitch pummelled by thundering boots
Lights flicker filling the arena dusk draws near
Legs chunky with padding play a legion of men
Skilful tricky whacking the sodden leather ball
Supporters gingerly balanced on slimy shallow steps
Applaud encourage lost in exhilaration
Protests, curses, exasperated whistle resound

Smoke spewed from proud chimneys drifts into view
Silent hovering tendrils tease passing phantoms
Boots clip clopping across worn cobbles
Costumed for necessity bland unassuming
Muffles caps dirty packs enshrouding stout heart
Blue marks of courage revealed on seamed cracked faces

Heads bowed low hunched backs
Muted conversation belying their fears
Approaching the gaping mouth, the greedy mouth
That will enfold, masticate and purge their labour.

# Pit Strike
## 1984-1985

Mary N. Bell

It was 5.30a.m. After a few hours of exhausted sleep I was awake again. The police! Please let them have abandoned the siege. I eased out of bed, crept across the bedroom floor, looked through the net-curtained window. They were still there, across the field, beside Station Bridge with their cars and vans. Hundreds strong, high helmeted, blue shirted police intent on stopping the flying pickets bringing help to their marras at Easington pit. Waiting.

Beyond Station Bridge the North Sea was briskly pushing waves to shore in all directions. No uniformity. White horses haphazardly leaping. The August sun already hot, sending flashing sparks off the water. The power of nature, watching.

One glance took in this familiar scene. I've lived in this colliery owned house in this colliery owned street for twenty years. My neighbours are the sea, the railway, the pit. I know the mood of the sea reflects the mood of the land.

I went back to bed.

I lay worrying about the agitation bouncing in from the sea. I listened to it. I was trying to get used to waking without hearing the clang of coal trucks racing across Station Bridge - noise that I never noticed till it was not there. The whistle of the engines and warning hoots from the pit yard were my background music. Now hollow silence echoed.

The bedroom window was open; a slight breeze from the sea rattled the catch. Alert, alarmed, a muted noise, strange to me - I couldn't identify it. I may as well get up. The alien sound drew me to the window.

I gaped. The field was full of marching, striking pitmen. Voices silent, their feet making the drumming sound, muffled by the grass. As they left the field for the road to the pit it did not empty. More men poured after them keeping the field full.

I dressed in a hurry. The gate slammed. My husband Jim, despite his bronchitis and despite being retired, was already on his way to the pit. As I opened the gate he was shouting from the bottom of the street, 'Hurry up! You've never seen anything like this except on the tele!' The pulley wheels were there in the background, black steel silhouetted against the sky-blue backcloth. Immovable.

What was out there was a lone pitman strike breaker, trying to get to work in the pit yard. The police had been helping him day after day. Pickets were drafted in from all over the country to keep him out. Hundreds and hundreds of police from all over the country were detailed to get him into work. Hence the police blockade on the main road at Station Bridge. The pickets outwitted them by leaving their buses at Horden and walking through the fields to Easington Colliery. A contingent of police was at the other end of the village too. Today they'd got the scab into the pit yard.

So I followed Jim to find as many as two thousand people assembled in the field. The noisy buzzing of angry voices hummed through the crowd and up through the gates.

Suddenly there was complete silence. Hundreds of pitmen in casual shirts and jeans crowded at the top of the sloping wasteland that overlooked the pit gates. The police stood there, immaculate in their summer uniforms, well-pressed trousers and imposing helmets with visors guarding their faces. Holding a shield in one hand and a truncheon in the other in orderly rows, they stood like soldiers ready for battle.

Power.

'Zulu! Zulu! Zulu!' The pitmen began to chant. The police rattled their truncheons against their shields, mimicking Zulu warriors. Policemen and pitmen alike had seen the film on tele that week about a Zulu war starring Michael Caine.

Then the stone throwing began. The miners surged forward. The police advanced to meet them. Someone grabbed a police helmet and threw it in the air. Gradually pit lad after pit lad was arrested. The police were in control. The prisoners were bundled into police vans that came from nowhere, sirens screaming. They sped away to police cells – so well organised.

The words of my father - dead a score of years - came into my mind; 'No good ever came from a pit strike'. He'd lived through the '21 and '26 strikes so I knew he talked a lot of sense. Every time there was an election, local or otherwise he quoted Churchill, 'If they don't work, shoot them,' referring to the miners.

The strike was about pit closures. My father had worked in many different pits – Black Prince, Hedley Hill, Hedley Hope, Sunniside and a few more that had closed. Eventually he had felt settled in Easington. He had called Easington a long life pit. He was sure he'd end his working life here but insinuated some would not. Still, he was also sure more pits would open as had always been the way, when one closed.

Coal would always be needed, my dad said.

I have every reason to dread pit closures with no new pits in the offing. My home, food, clothes and nearly everything I own has been bought with money earned at the pit.

That day the crowd dispersed. A few miners lingered in little groups, angry but not knowing how to cope with the situation.

The summer was hot. I'd never seen so many men walking about the place. Drawn to the pit, some would stand and look at the pulley wheels, still and silent. Others would dawdle slowly past as if unable to look the pit in the eye.

People used up their savings. They cashed their insurance policies. The sea was unnaturally calm. The horizon was invisible, behind a moving haze of silvery, dazzling mist which might be hiding some mysterious friend, or enemy or oblivion.

As the days moved on there were many scenes of violence, anger and emotion. Men were arrested for shouting at the police and other men were forced back to work through poverty and despair. One day there was a scuffle between a lone miner and the police in the middle of a crowd. He fell to the ground as he was being arrested. He lay face down. Some of the miners watched without emotion; others turned their heads away. The police pinioned his arms. No one helped him. This lack of support was the changing trend, caused not by fear of being injured or arrested, but by the overhanging threat of being blacklisted by the N.C.B.

Me? I took a photograph.

The summer turned to autumn. The weather changed dramatically. The north wind was so cold it just about cut your face off. Sleety snow, gale blown from the North Sea tasted of salt. Fuel became a necessity. Many wood fences disappeared. The wooded denes became bare. The young ones needed to keep their young ones warm. The trees would grow again. Coalmen toured the streets selling coal. Polish coal they said! Some said it was Easington coal. I tried not to think how it was acquired as I bought it. All pitmen received a coal allowance as part of their wages and were unused to having to think where household coal came from. Now they had no money to buy it.

I was lucky enough to be working. Through my job I met a lot of pregnant girls. One day a young woman arrived at the ante-natal clinic. Her baby was overdue. Her husband was carrying a toddler and they had walked seven miles. They had no money for fares. Desperation made them do it. They did not walk home. From then on we made sure all patients had their fares one way or another. One of my colleagues was adept at arranging lifts and making sure no one lost face.

March 1985. A strange dark cloud had been hanging over the sea for weeks. The water looked as though it was boiling and every now and again a huge rock was hurled from the sea, only to drop back heavily sending spray a mile high in the air. The mood in the village was reflected on the land; the miners were restless, some not wanting to give in, others wanting to get back to work for money to settle their debts.

This bitter, seemingly endless strike ended in March 1985. I stood on the crowded pavement and with a lump in my throat watched the pitmen of Easington parade down the main street to the waiting, open pit gates. The colourful pit banners fluttered and flapped in the spring breeze. Next came the colliery brass band playing a rousing march. The feet tramped in tune, a thousand men in harmony, not triumphant but unbowed.

Relief and frustration were on parade, reflected in grim expressions.

Union officials Billy, Alan, Bob, Dennis, in the lead. Jack the father of four, Joe with two, Keith with one, newly married at the beginning of the strike. Dull-eyed, worried faces. Marching.

The shopkeepers came to their doorways. Suddenly the mood brightened. People thought of pay-notes to come, bonuses to be earned. One man started to applaud the shopkeepers, and then another until the whole parade and the shopkeepers joined in. The men shouted their thanks to each shopkeeper by name for their loyal support as they proceeded. These traders had regularly given food to the soup kitchen organised by the women. They even gave two thousand pounds in cash.

Clapping. Marching. Faster tempo. Hop, skip, and a jump to the band. Appreciation shouted. The shopkeepers too had suffered. Not a dry eye on the route. Retired pitmen, women, and supporters wept – and I wept along with them.

This was no victory. The procession disappeared through the pit gates. It was over. If anything was gained from the strike I've not heard of it. The words of my father, a pitman for more than fifty years, still echo on my ears. 'No good ever came from a pit strike'.

F. Naughton

*Some of these miners were sacked by the N.C.B. and never employed in pits again.*
*They did not think that fighting to keep pits open would end in their being blacklisted.*

# Flag Day

Ann Peel

Hurray, it's Saturday. No train to catch, no school, no lessons, just fun!

Mustn't wake Doreen, it's only 6 o'clock. Mam is already downstairs, some precious time for just us two. The cat has had her kittens. I watched two being born last night. Can't wait to see how many new Blackies there are now. Quietly I go, along the landing and down the stairs, back along the passage to the living room and through to the back kitchen.

There she is, the best mam in the world. She already has the fire on and toast almost ready, the kettle boiled and the teapot on the hob to warm. 'Morning Mam, what time is it?'

'Just gone six, pet, you're up early?'

'Yes, wanted to see Blackie's kittens,' I said, as I stroked the object of my attention. 'I counted eleven little ones. I'm going to play with Joan and Ruby today. We're off to the beach to look for jewels!'

'OK pet,' she says. 'You need a good breakfast, cos you'll be out most of the day, won't you? I'll pack you some bait - cheese sandwiches alright?'

'Can I have a bit of your corned beef pie, Mam please? And some for Joan and Ruby too?'

'Think we're made of money don't you? But OK just this once.'

I set the table and wait for breakfast, watching Mam's quick and nimble hands trim the bacon and scramble the eggs and Italian tomatoes. She always knows what I like best!

'Can I do anything while I'm waiting mam?'

'What's up with you? Don't usually volunteer do you? But yes, can you open the front room curtains for me? I've not been through there yet.'

Back into the passage and along to the front room - special occasions only in here. All Mam's precious things and pretty crochet work, everything neat, not a stitch out of place. Pulling back the heavy brocade curtains, there's nothing quite like the swish they make and the sudden burst of sunlight - well, there is in July! Looking out, a double take, a frown, 'Eeh! mam, come and look here, it's a miracle I think!'

'Bit busy pet,' her voice came from the kitchen. 'Is it important. What do you mean, a miracle?'

'I think you have to see for yourself Mam. But next door's garden has grown flowers overnight.'

'Don't be daft man. That can't be.'

Mam eventually came, and gasped as she realised I was being truthful. 'Think we better see what your Dad thinks pet.' And she went upstairs to the front bedroom to wake him.

I waited to hear what he thought but all that reached me was the deep rumble of his complaint. Then I heard his heavy tread as he got out of bed and went to the bedroom window. 'Bloody Hell! There's going to be some trouble today,' he said, loud enough for me, and my sister Doreen, and my brother Ben to hear.

'What, Dad?' said Ben and I could hear them both running along the landing from their rooms.

'That can't be,' I could hear Dad mumbling, 'there was nowt growing there last night at ten, when I came in!'

I heard Doreen and Ben leaving his bedroom and him stumbling about, obviously getting dressed in a hurry. Mam came downstairs, walked across the living room and knocked on the wall and went out of the back door to wait for Mrs Stewart to come out too.

Ben and Doreen came downstairs and we watched through the window as Mam and Mrs Stewart talked in undertones over the backyard wall. Serious faces: our poor lady neighbour's face turned white and her bottom lip quivered as she went indoors.

Mam returned to the kitchen and continued preparing breakfast.

'Mam, what's going on?' Doreen asked. 'I thought it looked pretty. But can flowers really grow that quick? They are the prettiest purple too!'

Ben snorted and said, 'Yes and tall and not quite opened yet but they would have been perfect for the show at the end of the month.' 'What show, what's he mean Mam?' Doreen asked.

'Well pet, those are very special flowers, they are irises and later this month there will be a competition to see who grew the best ones. But these ones can't win, they'll be dead by then!'

'Well I think they can, they're beautiful,' my little sister responded.

Then the shouting began outside... Mr. Stewart! He was a little man but the voice was huge. He was really mad. Our whole family came back to the front of the house, but to the windows. Not even Dad, big as he was, dared open the front door. Mr Stewart wrenched the flowers out of the ground and threw them everywhere.

And that was when I realised there were no roots! Someone - we all said in unison "Sammy" - had cut the beautiful blooms off at ground level, brought them here and stuck them into the soil in their tiny front garden! I could hear Dad's stifled laughter upstairs.

He came downstairs and spoke seriously to the three of us telling us he hoped we would never embarrass him by doing something so daft. Mam said she was happy that she and Dad had stopped at three. Sammy Stewart was the youngest of eight children and by far the most unruly and spoilt.

Then we heard raised voices and looked out again. Once again Sergeant Jackson had arrived. Usually amiable and kindly, his face was stern and Mr Stewart was bright red, denying all knowledge of how they had got there. Mum said, 'I hope Susan can calm him down, he'll have a heart attack if this carries on.'

Sergeant Jackson spoke calmly and Mr Stewart regained control and they moved indoors to make the discussion a little more private.... ours weren't the only twitching curtains!

Three days later, The Mail reported that the July 30th Horden Flag Competition was cancelled, the majority of entries had been vandalised and found in New Third Street. The excitement didn't spoil my day though, it gave Joan, Ruby and myself something to talk about while we searched for jewels on Horden Beach.

Sammy Stewart was grounded for a week and that time was torment free, our own extended Flag Day.

# A Walk Through Time

## Chris Robinson

When I was a child I used to explore the coast in search of fossils, trudging through the clay-like matter that gave off a smell of sulphur. I imagined that I was lost in a swampland, being careful not to disturb lurking predators. I mined the caves for gold and found precious jewels in the rocks beneath my feet.

As I grew older my adventures continued, albeit on the pages of my notebooks. Yet my love affair with the coast was real. I would stroll along the cliff tops allowing the fresh north wind to caress my face. I would skim stones along the rippling shores or just stand and admire the rugged rocky banks.

Despite having spent so much time there, I've never really known how much history was hiding under the surface. Only recently have I learned about the fascinating past through the enthusiastic words of geologist Brian Young. He led a walk that my Mother and I went on one blustery morning in May 2009.

We met at the car park of the reclaimed colliery site and followed the footpath to the pit cage. I'd walked this path before, glancing at the markings along the way, but not really understanding the significance of it all. Brian Young's explanation was clear and precise. The footpath represents the old colliery south shaft. Its length from the car park to the pit cage is the same as the depth of the old shaft. The markings on the left show the periods in time such as the Carboniferous period and the Permian period. There are also markers along the way showing the different rock layers. These rock layers are the key to the past. They tell the story of Easington's progression through time.

During the Carboniferous period the land area, now known as Easington, was situated almost astride the equator. Tropical swamps, created by rivers flowing from the uplands and mud and silt deposits from the sea, covered the area where primitive trees, giant ferns and other vegetation grew. Over time the forest growth would decay and become buried by the sand and mud. New growth would emerge, decay and be buried and this process would be repeated for many years. While this was happening the land was slowly moving north. As it moved further from the equator the climate changed to that of an arid desert. Evidence for this may be found in the yellow sands found in the shaft.

Eventually the desert was flooded as the Zechstein Sea, now known as the North Sea, spread rapidly across the area. This flooding created a layer of marl slate between the yellow sands and magnesian limestone deposits found in the pit shaft. This layer of marl slate contains perfectly preserved fossilised fish.

After the formation of the magnesian limestone there are no rocks to show the events of the next 250 million years although the earth did carry on its journey north to where Easington is situated today.

But this was not the end of our journey through time. We headed away from the pit cage, across the railway bridge, following the beach banks to Hawthorne Dene. Along the way we were shown the fossilised or raised beach within the cliff face. This raised beach, we were told, is famous worldwide and appears in many geology textbooks.

Arriving at the Dene our guide brought us to 2.5 million years ago, when the polar ice caps spread across the land. At that time County Durham and the North Sea were buried beneath one kilometre thick sheets of ice. These were to melt over time and the climate would become as mild as it is today before freezing over again. This change in the weather conditions continued with the last freeze dating back to around 18,000 years ago.

We headed down onto the beach where our guide explained how the Dene was created by the melting ice caps. We then retraced our steps back through the edge of the Dene, along the beach banks and back to our starting point at the car park. This was a thoroughly enjoyable walk. It was interesting to learn about Easington's very distant past. I only wish that I had learned about it years ago.

# A Ride To Horden Beach

## David Lee

On the first Sunday in August I decided to take a ride down to the beach in Horden in an electric wheelchair. It was a lovely day, no breeze at all, warm, the sun was shining not a cloud in the sky. It was in the afternoon that I took off from Robinson House, drove down to Blackhills Road. It was busy. I had to keep an eye on what was going on around me. People were just stepping out and not looking to see what was coming towards them. A few times I had to stop to let folks pass.

Then I went to what was Fourth Street, now an open field, along to Cotsford Lane watching for cars, taxis and bikes. I then went into Alder Road until I reached the railway line. Over the other side were two schools and Stapleton Drive. It was hard to believe that this was once an open field and that Cotsford Park Estate looked onto it.

I went under the bridge. It was like stepping back into another world – quiet – maybe as it was years ago. On one side of the road there were all farm fields plus railway cottages and on the other a pile of old scrap cars. I have seen old photographs of what it used to be like, just an old track down to the beach and trees on the other side. I don't think much has changed from years ago.

Continuing down the bumpy road, I eventually arrived at the beach. I could hear the sound of the sea lapping onto the beach. There is a car park at the bottom of the road now. The watchtowers are still there as they were years ago, probably used by the Home Guard during the Second World War. Still as rocky as ever and still spoilt by the coal from the colliery – not a good sight.

I started to remember the times when my Grandma and I used to collect wood for her fire to use as sticks. Also the beach wagons would trundle down to the seashore to gather coal. A tear came into my eye. I think of what it was and what it is now. I know I am not the only one who has memories of Horden beach. With a lump in my throat, time to head back. One does not know whether he will come down to the beach again.

Maybe yes or maybe no.

*This story describes my own ride to Horden beach. I wanted to see what it looked like now.*
*My story also highlights the mobility problems of people in wheelchairs and scooters.*

# The Old School – Waiting

## Joan Wright

My purpose served, I stand and wait
And wonder idly of my fate
Old, decrepit, ill at ease
All I've left are memories
Children's voices, laughter, tears
Haunt me through these empty years
Those years long gone I witnessed much
The poverty with hope the crutch
The wars, the strikes, the spirit strong
The comradeship that lasted long
The saddest time when miners died
We weren't alone, the nation cried
And through my gates came children sad
Some whispering, 'I've lost my Dad,'
Uncles gone and brothers too
Every one of them I knew
When boys they too were pupils here
Bold ones, shy ones, all held dear
Within my walls a throbbing heart
Beat fast, I knew then I was part
Of Easington, how proud I stood
No more bricks, just glass and wood
The years went by the hope stayed fast
Prosperity was known at last
They did not think they could not see

That it would not forever be
Fast changing world, how hard they fought
Their final battle came to naught
The pit was closed, and faith then died
The miners watched and many cried
Then my time came, a child no more
Would come a'clattering through my door
Nobody wept, no fond goodbyes
They looked at me with empty eyes
For Easington had lost its soul
Without a purpose or a goal
To aim for, strive for, make a fight
It's now like me a sorry sight
Yes, here I stand my spirits low
Cracked playgrounds spurring weeds to grow
My windows boarded, ugly sight
But in the stillness of the night
I hear the laughter children's chatter
The hustle bustle and the clatter
Whistles blowing
Bells ring-dinging
Children in the halls all singing
My pride returns, 'twas not in vain
And Easington shall rise again

*The old school has long been regarded as an eyesore epitomising the decline of Easington.
Most people would rather it was pulled down. But as I walk past it I imagine a building with a soul: despairing, desperately
unhappy, but with the persistent hope that better times lie ahead for Easington and itself.*

# Travelling the Distance

## J.A. Bell and Mary N. Bell

*'In the early days when the school began when the child of the moment became the man..............We're going the second mile...... We're going the second mile!'* A. J. Dawson School Song c1940~1989.

An apartment in the centre of St Petersburg, Russia. A three-bedroomed detached house in County Durham, North East of England........ an Easington Colliery lad is the link.

In working on this project about Easington I spoke to many people - people who had been born and educated in Easington Colliery. Many were successful business people - dentists, tradesmen, teachers, a Member of Parliament – all high flyers, male and female. (I interviewed a young woman who was born here and educated at Easington Infants and Juniors then A.J. Dawson Grammar who is one of the highest paid women in the North East.)

All are proud of their roots. This is the story of James Bell, son of Mary Bell, leader of the Easington Writers.

'Born in Easington Colliery, educated in Easington Infants, Juniors and A.J. Dawson Grammar School, Wingate, I am what some may call 'working class'. It's true that the class I was a part of throughout my school life were workers. I am not a high flyer, I am not even talented, just a down to earth common or garden regular worker. I am not wealthy, I am not outstandingly successful in business but what I am is the product of hard work throughout my life and of taking the opportunities that life has presented me with at some time or other.

Some say you make your own luck, some say you are born lucky but in truth if you work hard you will put yourself into situations where opportunities then arise that you can grasp. So then you can move onward in your chosen career. This is my experience.

The key is self help. In my view you're not doing the work for others as it may seem when you are asked by your teacher, lecturer or boss to complete a set task. You are doing it for *yourself*. The product of your work is what gets you noticed, and that recognition is what then causes those opportunities to come your way.

So, I have come from small beginnings in Easington Colliery to travelling around the world, Holland, Germany, France, Spain, Japan, Mexico, USA and now living and working in Russia for the last 2 years. I work for a Multi-National Blue Chip company. *The Nissan Motor Manufacturing organisation.*

So how did it start? After state education, on to Further Education in the late 70s, New College Durham and Hartlepool College of Further Education. As you can see, it was no Harvard or Princeton; no Cambridge, Oxford or Durham universities. Just good old Further Education at the local Technical colleges as they used to be known: four years of day- release and twice a week evening classes during a four year Technical Apprenticeship with the Dutch Philips organisation at the Mullard, a TV tube manufacturing plant in Belmont, Durham.

This education and early experiences within the Philips's organisation gave me a good grounding in the Industrial Process Maintenance and Process Engineering environments. So now I am a respected Senior Engineer and Section Manager within the Nissan organisation

Of course all this is not 'sexy' as the terms is these days; it's not newspaper headline material but I have made a successful living out of it with and for my wife and two children who are now both married.

So I'm currently based in St Petersburg managing a multi-national section of engineers responsible for the engineering of the final assembly process producing the 3.5l Luxury TEANA & 4x4 X-TRAIL vehicles for the Russian domestic market.

Sitting in the business lounge of Schippol airport on one of my monthly trips back to the UK - being a regular flyer with KLM Royal Dutch Airlines permits me to be a 'Gold Card' passenger with a variety of benefits - I guess I could be forgiven for thinking I am successful.

You might say this is a far cry from the sports fields of the A. J. Dawson Grammar School and the Assembly Hall in which we sang the school song, sung at the end of each year to send a message to all its pupils - that you can make it, you can do what you want in life if you work to achieve your aspirations and build on your expectations and *go that second mile*!

I am going that second mile!'

**Editors Note:** *I have included James' story because he represents the next generation of this community who have used the resourcefulness and wit demonstrated in this book to make their way in the wider world. WR*

Mary N.Bell & J.A. Bell

# Dragonslayers

Terry Dobson

The rain washed all colour from the surrounding landscape, leaving it dull and dreary. The sea was grey, the skies grey, the ground a monotonous green and brown. They could barely see Essyngtana village two miles inland through the constant drizzle.

'Whose bloody stupid idea was this?' Uhtred grumbled. 'Standing on this bloody hill getting soaked. Can't see much of anything, never mind watching out for dragon ships! And even if we did, we'd never get that sodding signal fire lit, the bloody wood's wetter than I am!' He gestured with disgust to the pile of logs and sticks nearby, his fur cloak dripped and stank like a wet dog.

'Good! What a bloody stupid idea that signal fire was! Just what the dragon ships will be looking for that is. Light a warning fire, and they'll say, oh look, a fire, must be people there, let's go get them,' I raged. We were sitting there in the rain on the orders of Ealfred, our leader. It was the highest point for miles along the coast, ideal to keep an eye out for those damned Northmen. 'And you know how mad Ealfred gets about them.'

Uhtred spat and glared out over the sea. 'Ealfred's getting madder every day. He starts shaking and ranting at the mere mention of Northmen, and spends more time on his knees in the church than the priest does!' he said. 'He's definitely not the man his father was.'

I scanned the horizon carefully, particularly seaward. But there was nothing to see in the rain. It was true that Ealfred had become increasingly pious since Bishop Cutheard had granted him this land. And I suppose the madness was understandable, as Northmen raiders had killed his father and burnt his former home. Uhtred was right though, Ealfred was nowhere near the man his father had been. And if I were honest, I didn't even like him! But we'd sworn an oath to Ealfred's father to guard and protect him, so we were stuck with him.

Uhtred was complaining again. 'Do you know how long it's going to take to clean the rust off this mail?' he said, fingering his armour. 'And what are we doing, wearing armour anyway? It's not like there's going to be an attack. You know it and I know it. It's all just Ealfred's imagination. I could be sitting next to a fire getting drunk now, instead of wasting my time trying to catch a fever on this damned hill.'

I grunted as something caught my eye to the northeast. I dove to the sodden ground, dragging Uhtred with me.

'Hey!' he cried, 'What the hell?'

I pointed out over the sea. A black speck slowly drew closer. A ship!

Uhtred clamped his jaw shut as we watched from the top of the barren hill. It was unlikely that we'd been seen and I wanted to keep it that way.

The ship appeared to be moving south, and as it passed we could see the square sail and dragon-headed prow. It was definitely a Northmen raider. I thought it unlikely the ship would heave to anywhere nearby; the coast here was mostly cliffs, apart from the heavily wooded denes, and I doubted any sign of civilisation could be seen from the ship. Essyngtana was far enough inland, and the rain heavy enough, that smoke from its hearth-fires could not be seen.

'Should we try to light the signal fire?' Uhtred whispered, though the Lord knows why. The ship was way out to sea and we were the only ones around.

I glared at him. 'Are you really the idiot you look? If we did manage to light the fire, they'd see it and come straight for us! We're best off watching, and if they do turn in to land, then we ride our horses down there and warn everyone,. We'll get the men together and ambush those heathens. Surprise would be on our side, understand?'

Uhtred nodded, and glanced down at our horses at the foot of the hill. 'Uhm ... we may have a problem there,' he said. 'Your horse has wandered off somewhere.'

I sat up, threw my helm violently downhill and cursed my horse, the rain, the Northmen, and Uhtred, and anything else I could think of. I cursed again as I saw the ship turn towards the shore, heading, or so it seemed, for Hawthorn Hythe. I figured it would take them maybe an hour to get to the beach and start heading inland through the dene.

'Uhtred,' I said urgently, 'get on that horse and ride as fast as you can to the village. Warn them about the raiders, and get as many fighting men as you can. We can surprise them in the Dene. Meet me there. I'll keep an eye on this lot. And try not to be seen,' I ordered.

Uhtred nodded, ran down to his horse, and galloped east towards Essyngtana. It wouldn't take him long to rouse everyone.

I moved down the hill northward towards the Dene, its steep sides covered in trees and undergrowth. Plenty of cover there for an ambush, provided we had time to get into position. I kept my head down to avoid being seen as the ship got closer. As I got into position, I could see that the ship had a dozen oars on each side - so a crew of maybe twenty-five to thirty men.

After thirty minutes I could hear twigs snapping and clinking noises coming from behind me. It had to be Uhtred and the men from the village. With a low whistle, I got their attention, and they moved towards me. They were mostly armed with spears, a few with hunting bows, and they each carried an axe and shield. I whispered to them to take up positions on either side of the Dene and wait for my signal. The archers I kept with me. Uhtred took command of the men on the north side of the Dene, while I had the rest.

We could hear voices and grunts as the ship landed and the crew hauled it onto the beach. Then the crunching of feet on pebbles as they marched closer. Huge, shaggy shapes appeared dimly in the rain, getting closer and more distinct. Armour and weapons clanked as the Northmen approached.

We kept our heads down as they entered the Dene mouth and began to move in single file towards, and then past us. I nodded to the archers and they took aim and loosed their arrows. As the raiders began to yell, and several fell wounded or dead, we came at them from both sides. It was a complete surprise on our part and led to a brief, bloody struggle. Two of our men were killed, and five more wounded, but the Northmen were killed to a man.

We looted their bodies, taking precious chain mail and weapons, gold and silver arm rings, and everything else of value. We grunted and groaned with the effort, our sweat mingling with the rain. Our arms and backs ached from the strain of battle and the stripping of the dead.

Moving on to the beach we lowered the mast on the ship and dragged it into the Dene, covering it with branches and undergrowth so it couldn't be spotted from the sea. Where there was one dragonship there might be more, and there was no point in attracting attention. We couldn't burn the ship because the flames and smoke may be seen. Besides, we could probably use it or even sell it.

I sent two of the men up the hill to keep watch, and Uhtred and I hauled ourselves onto a couple of horses and rode to the village to report to Lord Ealfred.

I longed for some dry clothes, something hot to eat, and a soft bed. We'd earned them this day.

F. Naughton

*Ealfred did exist. He was the son of Britulfine, and went to Bishop Cutheard after fleeing the Vikings around 900 AD. The Bishop gave him the lands of Easington. During this time Easington was in a vulnerable position, as Vikings were raiding much of the coast of Britain. It is believed that Beacon Hill may have been the site of a warning beacon since Roman times, when it would have been part of a wider beacon network warning of Pict invasion. There is no reason it could not have been used as a look-out point during the Viking age. A Hythe is an old English word for Haven or Landing Place, and so Hawthorn Hythe (now known as Hawthorn Hive) was probably used as a landing place for fishing boats.*

# Beacon Hill

## Mavis Farrell

Highest hill on Durham's coastline
Teller of a thousand tales
Beacon blazes out a warning
Viking ships, Armada sails.

Silver seas delight and sparkle
Disguise the sound of sailors' cries
Many ships and men have perished
Souls sing as seagulls in the skies.

Weary farmers trudging homewards
To Blue House and the Beacon farms
Harvest is no time for leisure
They must fill the winter barns.

Easter children rolling paste eggs
Down the slopes of Beacon Hill
New white socks from Nellie Morgan's
Can you hear their voices still?

Back shift miners carry sea rods
Before their shift they fish the tide
Carrying cod and sometimes coalie
Sweet the gorse as home they stride.

To the south the wheels are turning
Descending men to feed the fires
Of industry forever greedy
Noise and dust pollute the skies.

Lovers laughing in the long grass
Can you hear their voices still?
Many of the population
Were conceived on Beacon Hill.

The farms are gone, no Easter children
No lovers laugh, no pit wheels turn
The National Trust now own the hillside
No longer does The Beacon burn.

*This is for The Easington Church of the Ascension Wives who so generously shared their stories with me.
Many of them are - The Easter Children.*

# The Jackdaw

## Susan Robinson

Beacon Hill draws Joe to it like a lodestone. He lies as still as a sunbathing hare in the short tough grass on the hill's brow. The thin earth on this bony skull of land has a bitter-sweet sap smell. This is his place. He's on top of his world here. The sea guards it from the east, stretching north beyond Seaham and then south where the land drops and the flights that tip waste from the three pits of Easington, Horden and Blackhall stretch like blackened skeletal fingers across the shore. He puts his ear to the ground and listens to the pulse of the limestone rock beneath him, and hears the pull and push of the sea, which sounds like womb sounds, and it makes him feel safe.

Joe has the 'sight'. He sees things that aren't there to others, ancient memories that echo through the bones of this hill. He knows it better than a history book at school. It gives him a sense of belonging to this land. He knows these things while he waits for his friend Tom.

Tom is wise in a different way from Joe. He shows Joe fox tracks and bird nests warm with eggs. He points out the up-and-down flight of the green woodpecker and spewed up owl pellets they find near fence posts. These two teach each other the things they know, but Tom finds it hard to be like Joe. It doesn't come natural, he says.

'Let's go get a Jackdaw instead,' says Tom.

'Me mam won't let us have a wild bird in the house. It's unlucky.'

'Aw! That's nowt. Keep it in the shed, man. Come on, I know where there's a Jackdaw's nest – the younguns'll not have their full feathers on yet. They'll be just right to take.'

They ride imaginary horses, as boys do, away down the slope of the hill, to clop down the wooden steps that lead to the railway line, then over and up the other side. They stop with a 'Whoah there' and dismount on the cliff top above Boaty's Bay. Then they slither down the narrow path cut into the side of the cliff to the beach below. Joe grabs onto clumps of grass to slow down and to save himself from falling head first.

They stand on brown sand struck with sun-bleached rocks and stare at a jut of land that probes amoeba-like to the sea. This is where the jackdaw's nest is: right at the top of a two-hand-span crack that splits the limestone cliff-face to the height of ten men. The fractured rock-front is sheared off, while the top narrows and threatens like the spine of a dragon's back as it snakes to the land. From where the boys stand the monster's curves covered by cruel brambles seem like sleeping green velvet.

'Don't do it, Tom! It's too high.' Joe can't bear to look at how far above the ground it is. He turns and skims flat pebbles across a smooth sea, counting five, no, six leaps with his best one.

'It'll be all right man. I've done it before.' Tom starts to climb the cliff. He seems to know what he's doing. He reaches, his hands grasp rock and feet jam into cracks. He hoists himself higher and higher. He's almost there when a jackdaw screeches out of the split limestone and starts to attack him. It swoops and swerves, mobbing Tom who curls himself to the rock face trying to hide. 'Help. Help. Joe! Do something.'

Joe throws stones. They miss. He waves his hands and screams. 'Get away, get away.'

The jackdaw flies at Tom. It claws at his head, wings flapping, shrieking.

This time Joe's stone finds its target. The bird retreats to a rocky ledge, to *caw-caw* its anger. Its evil black tongue sticks out of a gaping beak. And outstretched wings menace the air like Dracula's cloak.

'I can't move, Joe. I'm frightened. I want me dad. Help.' Tom wails.

Joe looks around, hoping to see someone, anyone who could help. He yells at the top of his voice. 'HELP.... HELP...' His voice bounces back to him from the cliffs; the thin echo of his words mock him. The only other sound is the sea that whispers a quiet in-tide to where the boy stands.

Then he is startled by a movement where the Jackdaw sits. He sees a withered woman sitting on the ledge. She smokes a clay pipe, taking long sucks on the stem. It's covered with froth like the cuckoo spit that hides the froghopper's spawn. She has a spiteful look in her eye. She spurts a vicious stream of tarry spittle towards Tom. She waits.

Joe's heart pounds, threatening to split open his chest. There's not much time. He knows that the witch-woman wants Tom to fall. He can't let that happen.

Trying to remember Tom's movements, he reaches upwards. His hands grasp rock and his feet jam into cracks. He drags himself bit by terrible bit higher up the cliff-face. He daren't look down. He daren't even look up. He asks God to help and promises he'll go to church on Sunday. He tries to match his ragged breath to the ebb and flow sea sounds that usually make him feel safe.

His fingers feel again for security in the rock. 'I'm coming Tom! Hold on.' He says the words almost to himself.

At last his hand touches Tom's foot. 'I'm here. I'm here Tom. You'll have to move up again. Go on, I'm right behind you. We can't go down, the tide's in.' He doesn't say there's a witch-woman who waits for one or both of them to fall.

He hears Tom crying. 'I can't Joe. I'm scared. That bloody bird. It was going for me eyes.'

'The bird's gone. Honest'. He hopes Tom can't see the Jackdaw from where he is. 'You can do it. Come on. Move! ' He pushes his friend's foot. 'We can't stay here all day, Tom. I want me dinner, I'm famished.'

Tom releases a sobbed breath that's almost a snort. It is this that gets him moving.

Now they crab-crawl, upward then sideward, making a tortuous way to the top. Finally they slide on their bellies over the cliff's dragon- spine down a grass slope until they are back on the beach, just above the high tide mark. They look at each other and each recognises the terror in the other's eyes. Joe's freckles stand out stark against his white face.

Then they start to laugh and their laughter sounds crazy. They rush home, their imaginary steeds left forgotten to graze in the field at the top of the cliff at Boaty's Bay.

The jackdaw circles its nest as it caws its victory. Of the witch-woman there is no sign.

*This came from an amalgamation of tales from a local man Jimmy Musgrave and of how he sees 'spirit.'*
*(He once saw a witch woman sitting in a gorse bush smoking), and the story of how my husband and*
*a friend went looking for young jackdaws down Boaty's Bay when they were lads.*

# Fear

## Agnes Frain

A knock at the back door, loud and persistent.

Barbara started; she glanced at the wall clock. One and a half hours to go. Forcing herself to take deep breaths, she smoothed her thin greying hair with shaking hands. Then, straightening her cheap blouse and, brushing an invisible piece of fluff off her skirt, she kicked her slippers under the couch. Checking her appearance in the kitchen mirror, she saw a drawn anxious face; she pinched her cheeks and bit on her thin lips to camouflage the pallor.

She made for the door.

Through the glass panel she saw two figures: one of them had his face pressed against the thick glass, distorting his features into monstrous proportions.

Pushing her feet into her shoes, she pasted a pleasant expression onto her face and opened the door. Two skinny pale faces with hooded eyes stared at her.

'Can I help you?' She kept her voice steady.

'Is Paul in?' the smaller one grunted.

She shook her head. 'Sorry, he's out. Went to meet some of his mates, said something about a game of snooker down the Welfare Hall.'

'Been there!' the taller one said.

Barbara tried to hide her surprise, the taller of the two, shaved head dyed a brittle blonde with a ring through the front of her lip, was a young woman.

'We've been there! Nobody's seen him since last night.'

'Well he must be in somebody's house.'

They continued to stand on the door step, stubborn and unmoving.

She grasped the doorknob, 'Are you friends of Paul's. What's your names?'

The young man stared, mean eyes glinting. He dropped his tattooed head and stood picking his ragged finger nails. His hands were large and nicotine-stained, too big for his skinny frame. His companion nudged him.

'I'm called Smeg.'

Barbara looked across at the grinning young woman, who sniggered. 'Me? I'm called Tash.'

Barbara stood to one side. 'He should be back soon. He'll need a rest before his night shift. Come in and wait if you want.'

She was aware of the large foot planted on her thresh-hold; no way was she going to let these young thugs realise she was fighting her treacherous stomach, a sick rolling sensation was gripping her body. Turning her back she walked through the kitchen into her lounge. Slowly they followed her. 'Sit down, make yourselves comfortable.'

The boy called Smeg sat on the edge of the couch; he lit up a cigarette staring in defiance. Tash wandered around the small room. Picking up a plaster ornament from the mantle-piece she turned it over in her thick, heavily-ringed hands. Then, giving a sniff of distain, she returned it to its place.

Next she turned to the book shelf where a set of well-worn paperbacks grabbed her attention. She flipped open a leather- bound book. 'The Holy Bible !' she snorted and flung it onto a chair. 'Are you one of those Holy Joes, then?'

Barbara shook her head and made an effort to smile, 'Two pounds from a charity shop.'

Silence.

Tash continued her prowling. 'When did you say Paul would be home?' She spun around, giving Barbara a menacing smile.

Barbara felt a shiver run down her spine and looked into the face of the scowling Smeg. 'Well then, are you in the football team, like our Paul?'

Smeg stamped his cigarette out on the carpet then ground it into the flat pile with his heel. 'Me! I don't play football, got better things to do.'

'Well, then, where did you meet my son, at the snooker club?'

Tash was preening in the mirror. She spoke softly. 'Around,' she said. 'We've seen him around.'

Barbara gave a little cough. 'Listen to me prattling on! I've forgot my manners. How about a nice cup of tea and a biscuit? It's about the time I put the kettle on.'

She glanced at the clock.

Tash and Smeg whispered to each other. The boy jerked his head towards the door. 'No. We've gotta go,' he said.

'Are you sure?' she said mildly. 'Well, I'll tell him you're looking for him. Sorry he's not here.'

'Don't fret about us, Missis. He'll come out of his hiding hole sometime. We'll hang around.' He stood and stretched, his jean pockets bulging.

Barbara followed them to the back door which they slammed as they left. She clicked the latch secure, and then, her heart pounding, she raced to the front door and turned the key.

Then she collapsed onto the bottom stair and wept. She thought of Paul as a boy, hiding from punches and kicks, too frightened to cry when his father, full of drink, had lost control. She thought how she'd decided that there would be no more of that violence. How she'd made a new life for her son, brought him here to the peace of a home without terror.

It was enough, they had survived.

She dragged herself upstairs, senses sharpened by the feeling of doom, of impending danger. She stumbled into Paul's room. The smell of sweaty socks and stale laundry filled his space. Clothes hung from drawers and books were piled in corners.

She snatched a small rucksack from the cupboard and stuffed it with socks, underwear, shirts, sweatshirt, trousers, comb, shaver, toothbrush and, last of all, his bank book. She rushed downstairs and peered out of the window. The street looked empty. She raced to the downstairs bathroom and opened the window to see the two of them standing smoking outside her gate.

With trembling hands she texted her son, *Where are you?* She'd have to wait for a reply. Then she went back to the front window to see that there was a man propped against the opposite house. No skinny youth this one, but a big hulk, smartly dressed with an expensive haircut. He looked sleek and polished. Drugs obviously paid well. Now he was speaking into a mobile. She watched as he nodded to other pale youths loitering on the corner.

She shrank from the window and tried again to text. No answer yet. Think! Her head whirled. She riled at herself, for God's sake get a grip! Brazen it out! With difficulty she controlled her breathing and shaking. Then she unlocked the front door, stepped onto the pavement and crossed the street. She stumbled. The ground shifted beneath her unsteady legs. Her feet caught in a discarded pizza box which she kicked away, muttering a curse.

A sudden breeze lifted the box and sent it scuttling down the steep street.

The smell of brine from the nearby sea, mixed with fresh manure from the allotments, wafted past. Barbara breathed deep this familiar smell of normality.

She nodded to the lounging man and said 'Nice day.'

Under his cold gaze she approached her friend's door. She rattled the letterbox and opened the door shouting, 'Jean, are you there? I'm off to the library. Are these the books you want returning?' She picked up the usual bag by the door, came out and closed the door behind her. As she passed him the man shuffled his feet and lit a cigar.

Toting the heavy bag she re-entered her home. She tipped the books onto the floor, shoved in Paul's rucksack and balanced a couple of books on top. She heaved up the corner of the lounge carpet, retrieved a slender packet of notes and pushed them into her coat pocket. Then she ventured out of her back gate.

Smeg and Tash were near the bottom of the street. The girl had her body pressed hard against the boy; they were sharing a cigarette, blowing smoke into each others' mouths. Their actions were blatantly sexual, challenging.

She walked towards them. 'Still here?' she said.

They glanced at her bulging bag with little interest. She turned her head as she sailed past. Swiftly now she walked up Seaside Lane towards the library. There were only a few people around. Most of the shops were closed, their heavy shutters acting as sentinels. A bus lumbered past; anxiously she scanned the passengers. No Paul.

She ducked into a doorway and looked back. Then, spotting no menacing figures, she pushed her bank card into the cash point. She tapped in two hundred; the machine clicked into action. With fumbling fingers she grabbed her card and money and rushed into the library.

She sat and watched the door, checking her phone for messages. Nothing. As she punched in the number for a taxi she prayed, asking for aid. She promised God she would be a better person. Just let Paul still be there!

Later she ducked down into the well of the taxi as it passed the corner leading to her street. Still she could see the group of skinny youths leaning over, talking through the window of a big car to the man in the suit.

When she got out at the police station the building loomed ugly, impregnable, tucked away, unseen by the milling shoppers that flooded the shopping centre. She looked towards the doorway and breathed 'Thank You God!'

Paul was being escorted out by a policeman who was patting his bowed shoulders. Her son was shaking the copper's hand but looked drained, exhausted. As usual he was wearing skinny jeans and scruffy trainers: the uniform of all the young men who hung aimlessly around the village.

'Paul!' she called.

Warily he scanned the area before walking towards her. She pulled him under a tree and thrust the rucksack into his arms. As he spoke his voice cracked with emotion, 'I had to do it, Mam. I know it was a mean trick just leaving you a note but you'd have tried to stop me.'

She pushed the money into his pocket and urged, 'Go on son, get a train, go as far away as possible.'

'But the police already knew about him,' he protested. 'They didn't need my information. They told me to go home and act as normal. They're watching him and his gang.'

Barbara held him, reaching up to stroke his fair hair. He towered above her, a strong sturdy young man. Tears of regret rolled down his face. 'Run, Paul, go! What do the police know? It'll all happen again if you stay.'

She took his phone, dropped it into a litter bin, thrust her phone into his pocket, then she turned away to hide her grief.

'Write to me Paul,' she said.

*I overheard two ladies talking in the supermarket about how one of their nephews had been threatened by drug pushers. They were tense and upset. This story sprang from hearing their conversation and is an imagined tale of how a mother might protect her child.*

# Poppies

## Mary N Bell

Poppies swaying
Opium loaded
Summer flowers
Heroin, cocaine
Oblivion

Poppies dancing
Fun gone wrong
Hooked, addicted
Needles syringe
Drugged

Poppies waving
Street fighting
Running naked
Control gone
Bliss

Smoke a spliff
Poppies dead
Living hell

Poppies swaying
Someone's child
Brother mother
Friend, lover
One of us

Human beings
Poppies
In the field.

*I wrote this having watched young people trudging about the streets drugged and seeing all the changes in them brought about by their addiction. Each of them belong to someone, and from the poppy fields come their tragedy and the tragedies of all their families.*

# Dreamer

## Chris Robinson

The snow lay thick on the ground. There had been another flurry before dawn, coating the drab grey buildings with a white glossy sheen. Sandra had been working a nightshift at the factory and was just setting off for home as the sky was brightening. Her brown suedette boots crunched through the snow as she gingerly stepped along Stephenson Way towards Thorpe Road. The smell of the chickens she had been plucking followed closely behind her. A smell which always lingered and which Sandra blamed for there being no man in her life.

The snow glinted and sparkled under the street lights, inspiring thoughts of the glitz and glamour of Hollywood. How she longed to go there. She often dreamed of what it would be like to become a film star, rubbing shoulders with the rich and the famous. She would dress in expensive gowns designed especially for her, instead of the faux fur and mock croc she bought from the Saturday market at Peterlee.

She was getting close to home now. Her stomach grumbled, reminding her that she hadn't eaten for a good few hours. She was looking forward to the hot breakfast her Mam would have ready for her. This thought gave her the fuel that she needed to climb up the bank to the top of Avon Street and home. The old wooden gate was unlatched. She closed it behind her and clumped up the steps to the back door. The kitchen was in darkness and there was no sign of breakfast.

'Mam,' Sandra called out.

The house was silent. She checked each room but there was no sign of her mother. The butterflies awoke inside her stomach, fluttering furiously. She hurried to the kitchen door, hurling it open, her eyes frantically searching. They fell to the ground and she noticed her footprints in the snow. Only hers, no others. Her Mam must have left the house before the last lot of snow laid. The butterflies had fluttered up to her throat now.

She skidded down the steps, across the yard and into the street. She knew she had to find her Mam but she didn't know where to start. She heard scraping next door and peered over their gate. Her neighbour was clearing a path through the snow.

'Mr Walker,' her voice wavered, 'Have you seen Mam?'

Mr Walker was in his late sixties. He was short and thin and smoked roll-ups. He looked up from his shovelling. 'No love, not since last night when I came in from the Victory.'

Sandra's mind spiralled as Mr Walker's words reverberated *'not since last night, not since last night'*. She hesitated no longer. She started her search at the allotments at the top of her street.

Her mind was a whirlwind of thoughts. Has Mam been out all night in the freezing cold? Mr Walker saw her when he came in from the pub, that's usually about eleven. It had snowed again before I'd come out of work. What if...? She stopped herself from finishing that last thought. As she continued her search past the allotments, along the yellow stone track towards Canada her mind drifted again.

'If only I were a rich film star. I could pay for Mam to be looked after. She wouldn't want for anything. I just wish I knew where she went on her wanderings.' Sandra was walking down the bank, away from Canada now, past the black iron bars that guarded the cemetery. She looked at the headstones marking each grave. It was always such a clean, tidy place. Probably the most well-looked after area in Easington. She thought that whoever took care of this place was obviously proud of their work.

Then Sandra stopped. She had seen a movement out of the corner of her eye. There were two figures sitting on a seat by the memorial garden. Only their heads were visible. One wore a green hat with a bobble on the top. They were facing away from Sandra but she knew it was her mother. Her heart jumped as she skidded around the corner towards the entrance gate, almost losing her footing on the slippery slope. She called out as she came nearer and the two figures turned to face her.

'Oh hi love,' her Mam said.

It took a moment for Sandra to catch her breath. 'Is that all you have to say? I've been worried sick. You weren't home when I got there and Mr Walker said he'd seen you last night when he was coming home from the pub.'

Her Mam smiled, 'He did, I waved at him through the kitchen window. I was making a cup of tea to take to bed.'

'But I thought you'd been out all night.' Sandra was exasperated. 'There were no prints in the snow.'

'I woke early and couldn't get back to sleep. I came out for a walk to clear the cobwebs away. It didn't start snowing again until I was passing the cemetery. Young David here saw me and invited me for a hot drink from his flask.'

Sandra had forgotten about the other figure. She looked at him now. He was tall. His hair was thick and dark, almost black. He had a kind face. Sandra smiled. 'Thank you for looking out for Mam.'

'Not at all,' he smiled back. 'Don't get much company in my line of work.'

'You must come to tea when you've finished David.'

'Mum, I'm sure he'll want to get home then.'

'No that would be fine. Home is even quieter than this place.'

'It's settled then.' Sandra's Mam gave David directions and left him to get on with his work.

Later they cooked and ate breakfast together then Sandra washed and went to bed. Her usual dreams of stardom never came, although she did dream of a gown made to fit. It was white and silky. She was standing next to a man with thick dark hair. He turned and smiled at her. He had a kind face.

# I Wanna Be (1)

## Susan Robinson

Easington Library 23rd April 2009 5-700pm

The library at Easington Colliery is a meeting place for young teenagers. It seems to have replaced the youth club that was pulled down several years ago. Although there is another place to meet at the Social Welfare Centre, the library attracts small groups; particularly girls aged 11-13 years. It's a safe place to be. The staff provide craft activities and biscuits and an agony aunt's ear to real everyday problems faced by these young people.

We meet with ten girls who are busy creating laminated placemats at the fortnightly craft club. Chatty and curious, they talk freely about their likes and dislikes; their fears and ambitions. The general consensus is that Easington is 'crap' with disgusting streets with muck and needles everywhere. They feel threatened and scared by 'druggies' and don't go anywhere on their own.

They tell us there is little shop choice, with none selling the things they want to buy - if they could afford them – even sweets cost too much. They are bored out of their minds, particularly on a Sunday when the library is shut. They complain that there is only the park and it's not really very good, although they like the new swing. But it's not like the park at Horden they say. That's the Best Park in the Whole World. They really would like a swimming pool. The one at Peterlee is a pound bus ride away. They are obviously concerned about money – or the lack of it.

They understand what needs to be done to make a difference. And are politically motivated but don't know what politics or politicians are. They decide that the old school should be pulled down and a new centre for activities created – of course to include the much desired swimming pool. In their wisdom they think that the old miners' houses should be pulled down to make way for new ones, but not bungalows, as there are already too many of them which are just for grannies and not for families. They say there should be more police to chase the druggies and the drunks off the streets. Their talk about this is open but not naïve. With one voice they say, 'we hate the druggies', but conversely don't mind peopled drinking as long as it's not on the streets.

Fame beckons, particularly since Billy Elliot and then the visit by the model and the photo shoot in the back streets. Perhaps it's shown them different things and a glimpse of some other sort of life to be had. Consequently everyone wants to be in 'The Best of Friends Show' on CBBC.

However, they don't relate to very much outside their own boundaries. The theatre is an unknown world. Museums are something perhaps visited from school. Art galleries are a foreign language. Music is something heard on an ipod, although one girl was learning to play the saxophone – but she originally came from Newcastle. Apparently to join the school band they have to have one year's experience playing an instrument. One girl says she's good with a triangle. There's a budding dark humour there.

With improvements they think Easington Colliery would not be a bad place to stay in as a grown-up, after all it's near to everywhere – if you wanted to go. They set their sights on staying here in spite of it all, several would like to become hairdressers and one even a shopkeeper if the place got better. One six year old was adamant she wanted to be a carer – perhaps looking after all those grannies living in all those bungalows Easington insists on building.

# I Wanna Be (2)

## Susan Robinson

I wanna be
A shopkeeper
Somewhere nice
Cos it's horrible here
I wanna be
A hairdresser
Me too!
But there's no money in it
So maybe I'll be
A lawyer
I wanna be a teacher
What?
No fear!

I wanna be
A carer
Although I'm only six
I know already
I wanna be famous
And change my name
To Sandra Dee
Or be a model
Like the one who came here
And posed
In the Billy Elliot streets
She was tall
With long blonde hair.

I wanna be
Lots of things
But I don't wanna be
Forced to work
Like in olden times
When kids looked like scuds
And were whipped with a cane
They didn't smile
Cos they were miserable
With just soup to eat

Because
It's crap here, like.

I wanna be
A person
And live with her -
She points -
Cos it's good with friends.

*This is my poem, inspired by the session. The words were spoken by a group of young girls at a craft session at Easington Library when they voiced what they thought they would like to be when they grew up.*

44

# It's Only Make Believe

The big drum booms, bo-boom.
The jazz band plays
*Here Comes The Sun*
It's actually finally carnival day
Hooray, the parade's begun.

Charlie Chaplin leads the way
Twirling a walking stick fast
Oh! Who's that I hear you say?
In black moustache and bowler hat
Yes, it's Emma? Hip Hip Hooray!

A tiger called Shanice
Prowls menacingly by
And pretends to growl quite fierce
Her striped face snarling with delight
As the crowd claps and cheers.

They stride along
To the sound of the drum
Two soldiers, proud and strong.
Quick march, Ben and Callum,
Smart in their camouflage uniform.

Two smiley red-nosed clowns,
With green-check trousers and big flat feet
Do somersaults up and down.
Katie and Megan such a funny treat,
Everyone's laughing all over town.

Look! CBeebies Folk, that's new.
Iggle Piggle and Macca Pacca,
Upsy-Daisy too.
But we know who they really are.
Olivia, Emily and Abbi, that's who.

Picachu from Nintendo
Goes by to lots of cheers.
A Pokemon that's yellow,
With black-tipped pointy ears,
Is really Amanda you know.

Everyone's in disguise you see
There's Jake as Homer Simpson,
And Callum as his friend Barney
With fantastic plastic masks on
They really, nearly fooled me.

Two red devils chase one another
With a pitchfork in each hand.
Little children stand and stare,
Scared at Millie and Teigan
But it's all in the fun of the fair.

A sugar plum fairy dances past
On ballet shoe tippy-toes.
In pink tutu like candy floss.
Pirouetting round she goes.
It's Emily, and she is not the last.

For Callum as El-Barto is
Bart Simpson's alter ego.
He runs around and plays his tricks
An alternative super-hero?
What a great parade - a terrific mix.

But what we would like to know
Is why it's all pretend?
For it never really happened so.
Easington Carnival came to an end
A long time ago.

And we won't have the chance to join in a parade
To be just who we'd like to be.
Ideas kept inside our head, costumes never made.
It can only be poetry make believe, never a certainty,
When taking part in reality is just allowed to fade.

*Easington Colliery Primary School Pupils:*
*Emma, Shanice, Ben, Callum, Katie,*
*Megan, Olivia, Amanda, Abbi, Emily, Jake,*
*Callum, Millie, Teigan, Emily and Callum.*
*Susan Robinson*

# Moods of the Moon

## Mary N. Bell

That damned indigestion that Tracy had been plagued with lately woke her up. The pharmacist had recommended a bottle of medicine and advised her to see her G.P. as soon as possible.

Tracy got out of bed and looked out of the window to the garden below bathed in moonlight. She looked up at the full moon. Its face was smiling at her tonight. Sometimes the big white face frowned or winked at her or just wept. She was influenced by the moods of the moon.

The bright moon - she had never seen it this bright - cast shadows across the lawn and illuminated the trees, flowers and bushes. All was still, peaceful and beautiful just like a black and white photo. The high fence cast a shadow over the garden bench. With a smile she peered at what looked like a figure sitting there - a man, his left arm stretched across the back as though waiting for someone to embrace. The figure looked like Mark. Oh how she longed to be that someone.

She glanced back at the man in the bed she'd just left, peacefully sleeping; her husband, good old Terry. She'd married him twenty years ago on the rebound. Bless him, he didn't know that.

She looked back again at the figure, sure it would not be there; it might have just been her imagination. But he was still there. Was it a trick of the moonlight? It couldn't be; the moon, shining brighter than a searchlight, lit up the figure and showed her it was no shadow.

It was Mark, no mistake. Mark, her first love, her first lover. For seven years they'd been together, four of them they'd lived together. Then she had become restless, thinking he was taking her for granted, thinking she had lost her attraction for him. So she decided to show him she was desirable. She went out with another man. Mark got to know as she'd intended but she wasn't prepared for the outcome. Mark left her, went home to his mother. She was sure he would come back.

Then he had moved in with Claire, one of her so-called best friends. The next thing she heard he'd gone out in his car, failed to negotiate a bend, hit a tree and was killed instantly. She went to his funeral in a trance, sitting at the back of the church. Claire was there alongside Mark's parents and family, where she Tracy should have been because he was really hers.

Then she had met Terry and married within six months. But even after twenty years Mark was always in her mind. She'd experienced second class happiness with Terry - no children. But he said, 'What does that matter? You've got everything I want.'

But she had never forgotten Mark and here he was in her garden. He'd found her again and come back to her as she somehow knew he would. Perhaps the body in the crash had not been his and he'd had amnesia for twenty years.

There was that indigestion pain again, more severe this time making her catch her breath and close her eyes. Opening them she looked down in the garden. Mark looked up to her, beckoning her into the moonlight. She tiptoed down the stairs, opened the front door and stepped out. Everything was so still, even the fountain which never stopped trickling and bubbling, was still. The ground felt warm beneath her bare feet, her pale, blue satin nightdress shimmered in the strange moonlight. Mark smiled at her and said her name. 'Tracy!'

She sat beside him, looked into his clear, grey-blue eyes. He took her into his arms. This is where she should be, where she wanted to be. She thought she heard voices singing in the background.

She whispered, 'Mark, this is Heaven.'

# The Old Woman and the Hare

## Joan Wright

A poor old woman lived a miserable existence in a filthy cottage. People shunned her, fearful that she was really a witch with strange, frightening powers.

How wrong they were. She had been a young servant girl, working for a wealthy family in a fine mansion near Darlington. Pretty, with long flowing golden hair, she soon caught the eye of their wastrel son who, mindful of the possible consequences, took advantage of her naivety and very soon put her in the family way. She was banished in disgrace to the workhouse where, some months later, she gave birth to a stillborn child.

Disowned by her family, she was forced to remain there where she worked as a drudge, toiling from early morning until late evening. Several years passed until, at her wits' end and fearful that the many beatings she suffered would either cripple or kill her, she stole a purse containing a couple of sovereigns. She took clothing she found drying by a fire and fled during one fine, moonless night. After hours crossing many fields and with daylight fast approaching, she changed into the grander clothes, pushing her own shabby attire into a hedgerow. She rested against a tree and then continued on her journey to where she knew not. She eventually reached Hartlepool where she found lodgings and employment in a factory.

She subsequently married. Alas, her husband turned out to be a ne'er-do-well who beat her and cavorted with women of easy virtue. Again, abject misery forced her to flee, and a kindly coachman of nodding acquaintance allowed her to ride on the stagecoach travelling to Newcastle. She alighted at The King's Head on Easington Village Green where she chanced upon a derelict cottage.

People told her it was supposedly haunted and hadn't been lived in for many years but, against their advice, she moved in. Her health was now poor and she sometimes feared for her sanity and was thankful to have a roof over her head. She cleaned it to the best of her ability and, with the little money she had, purchased some old furniture, bedding and a few items for the kitchen cupboard.

Approaching middle age, her hard life and various health problems had taken their toll and people assumed she was an elderly woman. Poor diet had thinned and whitened her once-lustrous hair, her face was lined and she walked with a slight stoop. She became forgetful and talked to herself; her mutterings and shabby appearance eventually giving rise to the belief among some of the villages that she was indeed weird and probably a witch. After all, who but a witch would live in a haunted cottage!

She was ultimately shunned. Only the Rector's wife and the local grocer showed her any real kindness – she now and again leaving clothing at her door, and he providing her with food and milk. The years went by and most people forgot that she was once a stranger to the village. The younger folk assumed Easington Village was her birthplace and fanciful children told tales of witchcraft and strange goings-on in her cottage.

A new Rector was now in residence and he and his wife seemed not to know about 'the halfwit' living in the run-down cottage on the village green. The grocer, now an elderly man, still kept a kindly eye on her and a religious-minded woman, fearful that she was an apostle of the devil, began leaving her own cast-off clothing at the cottage door, praying loudly as she did so for the wretch's soul to be saved.

Thus it was that one day, as the old woman was finishing off a meagre meal of bread and cheese, fierce barking was heard at her door and a hare came bounding through the hole at the bottom. It raced around the room in abject terror, then cowered in a corner, its pitiful gaze locking onto her own. Her enfeebled mind immediately felt an empathy with the poor creature. After all, hadn't she once been at the mercy of cruel, brutal men? She got up from her stool and hobbled to the far wall where she pushed aside a small chest of drawers, exposing a gap big enough for the animal to scramble through.

'Come, come quickly,' she whispered hoarsely. 'Quick, quick, get away.'

The clattering of horses' hooves and men's voices could now be heard, as well as the dog's insistent barking. The hare, its sense of danger at its peak, raced across the room and through the gap. The old woman pushed the chest back into its place. It was then she noticed the hare's blood on the floor from its leg which had been bitten by the dogs. She bent down and quickly rubbed some onto her leg, covering the rest with a ragged old mat. She tore a strip off her petticoat and sat down on the stool. She was bandaging her leg when three men burst through the door, preceded by the bloodhound. It made straight for the old woman, sniffing around her ankle, she trying to nudge it away with her foot.

'Where's the hare, old woman, where's the hare?' shouted one of the men.

The other two made a swift inspection of the two-roomed cottage while the dog still hovered around the old woman, sniff, sniff, sniffing.

'Where's the hare?' the first man repeated, gazing with revulsion at the woman's unkempt appearance.

His voice suddenly awakened within her a half-forgotten memory and she looked up, startled. She stared hard at his face. No, it couldn't be; it couldn't be he. But it was; yes, yes it was! She was gazing at the man who, years ago, because of his insatiable lust, had condemned her – a young, trusting innocent girl – to a life of hardship, deprivation and utter misery.

She saw that he was still quite handsome; yes, the years had been kind to the scoundrel, the face only slightly lined and the body still trim and upright. She muttered something inaudible and spat on the floor, narrowly missing his boot. She laughed mirthlessly.

'Let's go,' said one of the other men. 'It isn't here. Let's get out of this stinking hovel.' He and his companion made a hurried exit, calling out to the dog. It reluctantly followed them.

'Old hag,' muttered the remaining man. 'Stupid old hag.' Then he too made for the door.

'Bastard,' she shrieked after him. 'You ruined me, ruined me! A pox on your house, Sir. A pox on you and your family!' He strode outside and breathed in fresh clean air, her curses ringing in his ears. He mounted his horse.

'She's as mad as a march hare,' he said and they all laughed together as they galloped away.

The old woman died a few weeks later, her body found by the grocer, concerned that he had not seen her for some time. She was buried in the churchyard in a pauper's grave.

Of course people had been out and about at the time of the incident and had seen the hare being chased by the bloodhound and disappearing through the hole in the door. Indeed, one or two of the more curious had even stood in the doorway and witnessed the old woman bandaging her leg, with the bloodhound sniffing around her. And, of course, no hare was found.

And so a legend was born.

*This was inspired by a well known local legend. The children at school wear the hare as a logo on their jackets.*

# A Flash of Blue

## Mavis Farrell

Lydia leans her back against the safety barrier at the bottom of the steps, bracing so she can balance on her toes to get a better view. She stares intently as the bright stream of children ripple down. The late summer afternoon is an aviary of twittering voices.

'You've cut it fine today Lydia,' says one of the mothers.

'Mm busy, forgot the time,' she answers, distracted. 'I ran all the way down the bank to catch the bell.'

Lydia knows she worries too much. It's the guilt. Her youngest child is small, quiet, slow to reach milestones and struggling unhappily with her first term at school.

'She doesn't interact, rarely speaks and never joins in with the other children.' The teacher voiced her concern last week. 'Joanne is not like your other two.'

'She just shouldn't compare,' thinks Lydia. 'It's unprofessional, for a start.'

Now Lydia can smell perspiration under her arms and hopes that no one else can. She tries to strain higher on her toes so she can see the doorway, resisting the urge to go up the steps to get Joanne.

'Be careful children. Don't run. Go slowly down the steps and no pushing,' says Mrs Hall and she and the other teacher on duty, Miss Langley, smile complacently to each other as the children slow down.

It occurs to Lydia that Joanne is poorly, that the teachers will bring her down last. Perhaps she's fallen or been picked on. Perhaps she's upset. Lydia is hoping Joanne hasn't wet her pants again because if she has she won't eat any tea. The last few children straggle down the steps as the teachers turn to go in.

Joanne is not in sight. She's just not there. Not there!

'Where's Joanne?' Lydia is demanding.

Mrs Hall looks surprised. 'I helped her find her coat and put it on and I did think that she went down the steps. She may be in the toilets. We'll look there first.'

Joanne is not in the toilets. The school is being thoroughly searched. Mrs Langley is standing at the gates. 'Joanne must be in school somewhere because she hasn't come down these steps. I was here for the bell. I would have seen her.'

Panic thuds in Lydia's chest. She is feeling sick and faint. Her mind imagines the unimaginable. She is frozen. Someone fetches a chair. Someone else gives her a drink of water.

'We've searched the school and the yards. We must call the police,' states Mrs Lewis the headmistress, who looks more calm than she is actually feeling.

Lydia's vision is a blur. Voices sound distant. She can smell her own fear. It chokes her.

Two hours later Joanne is still missing. Police are searching house to house. Lydia is at home, being fed tea with brandy.

'Drink it up Lydia! Medicinal, for shock,' says Vera from next door, who has lived through a war and a pit disaster and knows all about these things.

The police woman fidgets. Young, nervous, inexperienced, she says very little and does less. Lydia's fear fills the room. Then the silence is shattered by six Westminster chimes.

'They're bringing Rob out-bye pet,' says Vera.

'No! No! Not that,' chokes Lydia. They must think it's a very serious situation. They only bring the men up from the pit if it's a serious situation. The two older children, a boy and a girl, stare at their distraught mother, who in turn stares into space. Then their eyes meet and they quietly get up and go outside. Lydia doesn't even notice.

By seven o'clock all three children are missing. By seven thirty all are safely home.

Lydia's son says, 'We went out on our bikes to search and rode round everywhere and on our way back. Guess what? We found Jo half way up the cemetery bank with two other girls, one about Joanne's age and one about my age but I don't know her from school. They were bringing her home because their Mam thought you'd be worried. Our Joanne's been there for tea and had pie and Angel Delight!'

According to Dr Carter, Joanne is not harmed in any way. In fact Joanne is a different child, very happy, very chatty and pleased to have made friends.

Lydia needs a sedative. Rob puts the children to bed. They all have an early night. The weekend passes in a blur of recovery and return to normality - whatever that might be. And enquiry.

'Did you come down the steps Jo?'

'Yes Mam.'

'Did you not see me waiting?'

'Yes Mammy.'

'Why did you pass me?'

'Because Lilly and Annie asked me for tea and they're my friends.'

'Where do they live, Jo? Can you take me there?'

No answer. In fact no more talking at all for two weeks.

Mrs Lewis can shed no light on the situation. There was neither an Annie or a Lilly at Easington Colliery Infant or Junior Schools. The headmistress wonders to herself if Joanne made it all up. If so where had she been for those four hours? She also wonders why Joanne chatters away happily to herself and not to the other children. Later, she was to wonder if a referral to the Educational Psychologist would be necessary.

Two weeks later Joanne is asking her Mam if she can go to see Lilly and Annie. 'I've been asked to tea again. They were at school today.'

'Yes, love!' said Lydia, suddenly alert. 'I'll have to come with you though, but you can lead the way because they're your best friends.'

Like a happy puppy eager for a walk, Joanne hops and skips down the cemetery bank, round the corner into Crawlaw Road. Lydia is anticipating her meeting with the girls' mother.

The pithead rattles and clanks, never quiet even at weekends. The September sun sparkles on the sea and on the wings of the homing pigeons as they sky sail over the allotments. Everything shines silver.

Joanne turns without hesitation down the back of Ayre Street, the terrace of colliery houses leading steeply down in the direction of Seaside Lane. A boy rockets past them on a skateboard, swerves under the white sail-sheets pegged on a line, and out of sight. Most houses have tidy yards with whitened steps, winning the constant battle with the coal dust.

Joanne stops half way down the street and points to a paint- peeled gate hanging open on one rusted hinge.

Lydia frowned. 'Are you sure Jo, is this it?'

Joanne slips through the gap. Lydia follows.

The backyard is heaped with litter, some blown, some thrown. It piles up in triangles in the corners. A bee lands on a bright dandelion, one of many growing in cracks between the rubbish and shards of glinting broken glass. The door and windows are boarded up - nails not new but rusted with age.

The bee drones on its way to another flower. Joanne watches it intently.

'What do you want in there?' An old woman stands in the next yard looking over the low wall, wrap-around apron stretched tightly, arms folded confrontationally across her ample breasts.

Lydia and Joanne jump simultaneously. Joanne sniffs and sticks out her bottom lip. It wobbles a bit.

'Err um, we're looking for two of my daughter's school friends,' says Lydia. 'She thought that they might live here.'

The ample woman shrugs. 'Nobody has lived here for many years, not since the fire.'

She glances in Joanne's direction, beckoning Lydia forward. 'It was a terrible thing,' the woman whispers. 'The mother - such a nice young lass - went down to Burdess's to buy pies for their teas. When she got back, only minutes you understand, the house was a raging fire. We all had to move out and be repaired. We weren't safe.' She nods. ' The two little girls were trapped upstairs. Didn't stand a chance. The mother blamed herself, like.' The woman looks again across at Joanne who is busy picking the dandelions now that the bee has gone. 'Poor lass hanged herself and her man moved away. He blamed her of course and she blamed herself. No children there since them canny bairns. Bonnie they were, one about *her* age...' she nods towards Joanne'... and one a bit bigger.'

Stunned by the sad story, Lydia nods to the woman and leads Joanne back out onto the back street. 'Your friends' house must be further on, Jo. We'll walk down a bit.'

Joanne recognises none of the other houses. 'It was that one Mammy, the one we saw...' is all she will say. They turn the corner and walk up the front of Ayre Street. Children are playing rounders on the green. 'Can you see your friends over there?' asks Lydia.

Joanne silently shakes her head.

The day changes. A cold damp sea fret is snaking its way up the colliery streets, softening the shouts of the children and the grinding of the pit.

As they pass the empty house, Lydia notices some boards have fallen loose from an upstairs window. It may only be a trick of the light but Lydia is almost certain she sees a movement. A small brown arm. Perhaps a flash of blue.

# Tunnel Vision

## Agnes Frain

Nan pounded down the stone staircase leading to the changing room. The outpatients clinics had run late again. Rushing past colleagues who were changing into their outdoor clothes, she delved into her locker and pulled on her jeans and jumper. Her fingers fumbled in her haste.

Driving out of the hospital grounds, she headed for home, seven miles away. Would he wait? She was tense and anxious, thinking, 'Is he at this very moment leaning on the railway bridge waiting for my arrival?'

She pressed the accelerator praying that there were no police vans with their hateful cameras ready to pounce on harassed motorists. She sped along the road. 'Five thirty, come on come on,' she muttered. 'Get a move on!' The driver in front ignored her plea and continued to creep along under thirty miles an hour. Sweat began to trickle down her back. Would he wait? Or give up on her and tramp home.

At last, she reached her home village and began to negotiate the steep streets of Horden, full of terraced houses that led down to the sea. Destination reached, fingers crossed that she wouldn't rip off the exhaust, the car bounced and rocked at walking pace over the rutted neglected railway bridge.

There he stood, chatting to a group of men. His eyes sparkled as he watched her progress. Nan lowered her window to wave at him. She could smell the strong smell of manure and the potent smell of compost heaps. Pigeons circled above the gardens. The rattle of corn in tins and soft whistles guided the birds to their home lofts. Sunbeams spun webs across the dirty windows of patched up greenhouses, the sea glowed in the distance, a bluebell blue. White clouds created castles in the light sky.

Aware of eyes that assessed and calculated, Nan began her multiple point turn. The men moved away from the bridge and lined up against one of the rough fences that edged individual allotments. Watching. Embarrassed, she took special care in case she nicked a corner of a fence.

Nan wiped her damp face with her jumper sleeve and pulled at the high neck. Once again she had chosen the wrong outfit because of the coolness of the morning. The audience was silent. She stifled a giggle. If I dare hit anything - bang bang, I'm dead!

Manoeuvres complete Nan sat with her car facing towards the bridge ready for the return journey.

He saluted the firing squad and wandered over. The men began to dispense their tatty carrier bags full of the bounty of the lush and productive soil. His outfit of overalls and a dirty jacket did little to distract his natural grace and granite features.

Then he opened the car door and eased into the car, his arms full of freshly cut flowers. 'A bit late, pet, I was just about to leave.' He grinned at Nan. She gritted her teeth as she rattled back over the bridge.

Nan glanced at the flowers. Not for the first time she wondered if they were for her. He must realise she liked flowers and every colour of the rainbow lay on his lap. The dirty brown bag tied around their stems emphasised the beauty of the bouquet. Perfumed smells filled her car.

Oblivious to her wishes he chatted, then waved and smiled at his fellow gardeners. The vehicle groaned in protest as she forced it to climb the steep streets.

Nan pulled up outside the house. She watched as his sweetheart waved and blew a kiss towards the car. Out he clambered, flowers still in his arms, his handsome lined face beamed.

'Oh I forgot.' He bent to look at Nan through the window. 'These are for you.'

At last! she thought. Bringing a battered brown bag from his pocket, he placed it on the front seat. She knew it would be full of over-ripe tomatoes so soft they could stick to walls.

Sighing in exasperation, she watched as he opened the garden gate and walked towards the woman. He gave her a kiss and placed the flowers into her outstretched arms. Nan observed her pleasure as she stroked his head with gentle touches.

Nan's eyes filled with tears. She lowered the window and shouted, 'See you tomorrow Mam, I'm off duty.' She tooted the horn.

Her parents waved and smiled at her as she drove away.

F. Naughton

# The Pigeon Egg

Susan Robinson

His wife is ill
Two months they say
So they go back home
He brings a gift
A pigeon egg
Look, he says
It's perfect, full of life
Full of hope
And later in cupped hands
He shows
The hatchling
Ugly, light as down
All beak and eyes
And big red feet
It's yours, he says
Called Hope.

Hope grows
Brings changes
Feathers
Bruised blue appear
With iridescent rainbow trim
To promise time
Of flight
And his wife sits
Propped in a chair
In the sun
Near the pigeon cree
While he works
At what he loves
And knows best
Trying to make sense
Of everything.

Hope won't go
Won't fly
He tries
Each training toss
A failure
He doesn't understand
So lets the bird
Stay with his wife
Because there's little else
He knows to do
She pats his hand
To thank him
And pretends to read
To make things
Seem normal
For a while

There's less of her
Each day
Less of her look,
Her voice, her smile
She tries
She doesn't fail
Because now he knows
And understands
Those that fly must fly
And Hope lifts its wings
To disappear
Into the sky
He reaches high his hand
And strains his fingers upward
And shouts
Howay, Howay.

# The Killer Rabbit

## Terry Dobson

'It'll be company for the guinea pig,' Dad was saying as Fred, our big tomcat, yowled in surprise. Fred had been sniffing the rabbit Dad has just brought home when it had kicked him. Fred gave the monstrous long-eared creature a look of disgust, then turned his back on it and sauntered away, head and tail held high, as if to deny anything had happened.

The albino rabbit that now stood alone in the centre of the yard was enormous and its pink eyes gave it a demonic cast. Our mongrel dog Bryn gave the rabbit one look and fled into the house. Maybe he wasn't so stupid after all.

The elder of my two sisters was talking baby talk to the rabbit as she went over to stroke it. 'Awww it's cute, let's call it Snowdrop,' she said, her hand reaching down. A second later, her hand was bleeding and she was crying, and the rabbit was alone in the middle of the yard again.

Dad just laughed and bent down to pick it up. It was kicking and biting as he put it into the hutch with the guinea pig. The next day my sisters were crying. The guinea pig was dead in the corner of the hutch, squashed in the night by the weight of the huge rabbit lying on it. Snowdrop was chewing nonchalantly as though nothing was amiss, like a miniature long-eared polar bear from hell.

Dad wasn't laughing now.

Snowdrop had the run of the yard, as none of us would go anywhere near him. The dog cowered away and the cat just pretended Snowdrop didn't exist, except that he walked along the wall around the yard rather than cross it. The boy next door would lean over the wall and laugh, but I noticed he wouldn't get too close either.

One morning we woke and the rabbit was gone. Snowdrop had kicked his hutch to pieces and made his escape through the open gate. We didn't look too hard for him. Actually, we didn't look for him at all. That rabbit was big enough and nasty enough to look after himself.

My only concern was Snowdrop's offspring. Would Horden one day be invaded by a plague of killer white rabbits?

# The Biggest Darts Game Ever Played

## David Lee

On the 31st May 1976 a darts final was about to begin, between two teams of the Friday night darts league. They were The Deputies and Rugby Club both situated in the village of Horden. They were equally matched. They are going to fight for the top place of the league, and this will be a fight at the Club.

Before it was altered, The Rugby Club had a long bar with seats all around the room. The walls were wood grained panels. In the middle row of tables is where the domino players would sit to play their games. Also in evidence was a pool table this was always used, Not forgetting the Smokey.

A haze of people's pipes hung in the air. The lounge was used for regulars to have a chat with their own friends and wives. At seven o'clock the doors opened and the members started to arrive at the club, for the biggest game of the season.

Soon the home team had come into the club, bought their drinks in and started to practise on the dartboard. These visitors had arrived at the club with a look of determination on their faces.

After we all met a practice session started to warm up the players.

It was now make or break time. Everyone came into the bar, even the members from the lounge. The domino players put down their dominoes. To support us the atmosphere was electric.

The scorer Paul called the two captains to the 'oche'. They had both been on top of their game. The club went a deathly hush. You could hear a pin drop.

Steve won the toss and started the game.

'180!' Paul shouted.

Terry replied with the same score.

Steve rallied again with a100.

Terry matched that.

380 was left to score. Terry threw a fantastic 180.

Steve replied to match that.

Each player was left with 100 to win Steve threw his darts, scoring 60.

Now it was left to Terry, who threw a score of 80. Double top left.

Next it was Steve to throw He could only score 20. His other dart missed the wire. Then a cry of relief as Terry hit D20.

It was a very warm night outside, the sun was streaming through, the windows and doors had to be opened.

It was now 3-all.

Yours truly had to play the decider. What a game I would have to play. The pressure was on my shoulders.

As I came to the 'Oche' perspiring all over, fear coursed through me. It had to be a good result, I could not let my team down now. I won the toss.

'180!' Paul shouted. A huge cheer went up which seemed to unnerve John. He could only score 100!

I scored again. 180!

He came to the board and 180 was his score.

This means 100 was left to win. John needed 160 to win. 120 was his score.

Tension through my body caused an adrenalin rush. When I came back to the board everyone shouted to drive me on, Then there was an eerie silence.

The first dart hit the wire, I only needed 60 to win. I scored 20. That meant double 20 to win the game. The first two darts hit the wire. Do or die time!

Then I'd done it. We were top of the league.

A mighty roar filled the club. Every one congratulated me.

Now, food came out - sandwiches, pies, sausage rolls, even cheese and onions.

What a night to remember! This has got to be the biggest dart game I have ever played.

# Picketing or Not?

## Mary N. Bell

I breathed in the fresh air and held it in my lungs. Now for the cigarette. Thank God that shift was over. Stepping out of the pit cage into the bright sunlight, after eight hours underground, I screwed up my eyes. The coaldust filled air smelled sweet even though I still had the stink of the pit clinging to me. A dank inhuman smell, mixed with sweat and even worse things.

Just think. I only went to work down that hole to get security for Jeannie and the kids.

I moved half a brick and took the match and cigarette I'd hid there before the shift. Then I lit up and breathed in deeply again, inhaling the welcome taste of tobacco, comforting, bringing normality after being next door to hell. I always looked forward to this cigarette - no smoking down below.

I went with the flow of men to the lamp cabin to hand in my token and lamp. We were all in a good mood, the strike of '74 and '75 was over. Better pay to look forward to!  The attendant handed me the note that was to change my life. 'It says you have to go straight to the manager's office before you get showered,' he said.

'Oh-oh-oh-oh!' The men's voices came in chorus.

'Been a naughty boy then?' said one of them.

I hurried to the office, wondering what on earth the manager wanted with me. I'd done nothing wrong as far as I knew. Nevertheless my heart was beating a tattoo. Black as a crow, with pit dust and smell clinging to my face, hair, hands and clothes, I knocked at the pit manager's door. It opened. I held my breath.

'Bill Hanson? Come in.' It was a stranger.

'Stand over there.' Already I felt at a disadvantage in my pit dirt.

A camera flashed.

'Can I have two of those please?' I joked.

No one laughed.

'Sit down!'

I sat opposite three clean, immaculately-dressed men and me in my old pit clothes from a jumble sale. At least my pit boots were new. This lot smelled of Calvin Klein aftershave, me of the stinking pit.

'We are police, C.I.D,' said the largest of them. 'We want to know why you didn't come to have your photo taken when all men who had picketed during the strike were asked to come?'

'I didn't go picketing. What's this about?'

'We'll ask the questions. Do you know the area Normanby Flatts and the Eston Hills?'

'Yes.'

'How well? Do you go there?'

'Yes, my sister-in-law and her daughter live there.'

'So you go there often and know the area well.' A statement not a question. 'So you will know that a murder was committed on Eston Hills?'

'Yes.'

'I'll ask you again, did you go picketing on the day of the murder?'

'No.'

'Are you the only Bill Hanson who works at the pit?'

'As far as I know. Yes.'

'We know you are.'

Why bother to ask me, I thought?

'Are you sure you didn't go picketing that day?'

'No, I've told you.'

'How do you know you did not go that particular day?'

'Because I never went picketing at all.'  Would they never stop trying to wear me down?

Opening a book the larger detective remarked, 'How is it that your name is in this book on the list that shows you were picketing on that day and it is marked paid? You were paid for picketing and other days before that.'

'No.' Now I was worried. My name on a list!

'We have no choice but to take you into custody to question you at Peterlee Police Station. This is very serious Mr. Hanson.'

'No – ask the union men, ask my marras! They'll tell you I never went picketing.'

'This list is from the Union Officials. This is looking very serious for you. Think very carefully.'

Feeling very puzzled, I was taken to the pit baths escorted by two policemen. They say they will tell my wife.

'Can I not see her? I'm taking her out tonight. *She'll* tell you I never went picketing'.

They let me get my shower and I am taken into custody. I can't believe this. I am being accused of murder and worse – rape! Not me, I'm a one-woman man. My wife and family are my world.

'Your wife can't visit you till we've finished questioning you and charging you.'

She'll be so worried.

I'm being locked in – is it a dream – a nightmare ? No, it's happening to me! Questions and more questions.

They brought up the fact that I had killed during the war, thirty years ago. But that was different. Then there was that time after the war when a kid had rolled the bin lid against the back door and I ran out – like a madman, they said - and caught the young lad and shook him and threatened him.

Well, I was bomb happy, then. Shell shocked - had battle fatigue whatever you like to call it. I'm all right now.

Then there was the time someone had taken my cigarette from my hiding place. I gave my marra a good hiding for that.

These police know everything. They have certainly done their homework. Anybody would have a short fuse if such things happened to them.

'A cup of tea – something to eat?' The thin one says.

'No, I just want to go home to my wife and kids.'

'Just admit you went picketing.'

The longest night of my life was in that lonely, cold police cell. Things looked bad against me. I'd never felt so alone, not even when I was on watch in the middle of a pitch black night in the Med. Why did they not believe me? How were Jeannie and the kids? Had I been set up? What if I said I *had* been picketing? It might look worse. Could it be any worse? I thought this was a free country. I had to stick with the truth. I did *not* go picketing.

How are Jeannie and the kids? Worried to death – like me. No sleep for me tonight. What will happen in the morning?

The next morning, the cell door opens. What is going to happen now? My heart is beating fit to burst, my stomach in knots, my mouth dry. I can hardly breathe. I need a shave and a shower.

The big policeman is standing over me. 'You can go home now, Mr Hanson. The killer's been caught. Aren't you lucky?'

Lucky! lucky! – locked up in a cell all night like a criminal. I never went picketing. Who was it, I wonder, who put my name down and collected the money?  I might just kill him.

Mavis Farrell

# The Stolen Man

## Mavis Farrell

One time muscular and slim
Broad of shoulder
Straight of back.
Proud of a shift well worked
And a job well done.
Supping pints with other men
United
In a common goal
The coal.

Who is the stranger
Coughing there
Breathless in
His TV chair.
His marras now
Are Morse, Frost and Poirot.
Hearing aids and metal knees
Creaking neck.
Companion constant pain.
What was the gain
The coal.

Coal stole my man
And yet,
His mind's the same.
Memories treasured
Spirit lifted.
If he could live his life again
He'd choose the pit
He'd do the same.
It must be bedded
In his soul
The coal.

*This poem was written to demonstrate the heavy price paid for coal by the men who mined it and reflects on their lack of regret and the buoyancy of spirit which endures.*

# Endurance

Susan Robinson

Margaret puts the shoe box on the table. Under the crinkled tissue paper lie the most beautiful shoes she's ever seen, palest pink with bugle beads and lilac sequins, iridescent like oil slicks in the rain: shoes made for going places. She can't resist looking at them, as she's done umpteen times since she found them at the jumble sale at the Ascension Church Hall last Friday.

*Get them shoes off the table – it's unlucky.* She hears her mother's voice in her head. Or it might be her own voice. Sometimes she sounds just like her mother.

The ritual of Sunday Dinner is over, thank God. Mam appears to sleep in her chair, although Margaret knows this is a way of spying on her. It has to be so for, as soon as her own backside gets near a seat, her mother wakes. *Get me another cushion, pet. I'd love a cuppa; put a slosh of brandy in. Oh, my aching back, where's the pain killers? I need the lavvy, bonny lass, be quick.*

She's told that it's the stroke of course. But wasn't it always like this? Especially since Dad died. *Look after your Mam,* he'd said. That's what you have children for, you know? Someone to see to you in your old age. But at forty-five, Margaret's own old age rears its own ugly head – and she wonders who'll be there to look after her?

She reaches for a cold Yorkshire pudding, tucks a large piece of roast lamb inside topped by a dollop of mint sauce. She stands with her back to her mother, staring out of the kitchen window as she stuffs the food in her mouth. It's nearly two o'clock. Won't be long now. Her heart does the collywobbles at the thought.

'Don't you think you're fat enough?' The words startle her, jostling her hand, catching her out.

She swallows the half-chewed bite, turns and smiles at her Mother.

'I know Mam. Wish I could be like you. Nice and slim.' She brushes herself down, feeling the offending rolls of fat through the thin cotton of the wrap-around pinnie that was once her mother's.

'You take after your Dad's mother. She was huge you know. Died young, she did, I'm telling you. Listen! Is that the band? They're early the day. Help us to the sitting room pet, I can hear better there. Eee! I don't know what I'd do without you, you know.'

There's plenty of time. The Sally Army always plays two tunes before they come knocking to sell The War Cry. Her heart bangs in her chest, rat-a-tatting in time to the gospel music that sidles into the house.

'*Stand up, stand up for Jesus, Ye soldiers of the cross. Lift high His royal banner...*' Mother's breathless voice wavers along to the tune.

Margaret thinks about the trumpet player who joined the band a few weeks ago. He moved in next door, to lodge with Mrs Gillespie, who was in the Sally Bash too, so didn't mind him practising his music. He was the one to sell The War Cry lately. She remembers the first time he'd stood on their front step. 'Hello,' he'd said. 'I'm Tony; I hope I haven't disturbed you with the trumpet playing, you know, next door.' He jerked his head towards number nineteen.

'No. You're... I mean, it's lovely. I like a bit of ...er... jazz.' She was good at pretending.

'Well, I can't play hymns all the time can I? Like to play the field so to speak. Mrs G. doesn't mind. Says it reminds her of her hubby.' He took her money, then smiled and moved on further along Station Road.

That smile stayed with her all week, flashing its perfect Jess Conrad teeth at every moment.

The time after that he said, 'It's Margaret, isn't it? I hear your mam shouting you. Keeps you on your toes, eh! I'll bet you're a good dancer, light on your feet after all that exercise.'

Oh! A bit of flattery went a long way. She has taken to twirling about the house and doesn't grumble so much under her breath about her Mother. The music he played changed, became softer, more romantic. Strains of *Moon River* and *Rhapsody in Blue* filled her days. He's playing these for me, she thought, as she swayed through the housework.

The next week their hands touched when he took the money and gave her the newspaper. The shock tingled her spine. But she noticed how he looked at her, at the dinner-stained pinny and her mother's old stout shoes on her feet. Not shoes for dancing, those.

This made her stop and think. Oh God - she was turning into her mother. But isn't that what women do, she thought. Especially single women like her.

*'Holy, holy, holy; merciful and mighty! God in three Persons, blessèd Trinity!'* Her mother's wavering voice.

The knocking comes to the door. She has to take her chance. She whips the pinny off. Underneath she's splendid in her best frock, all pinned, tucks and frilly bits. She slips the beautiful shoes on her feet and answers the door.

'War Cry, Missus?'

'Oh!' It's not Tony. 'Where's Tony?'

The older man with the Stewart Grainger hair looks at her. 'Tony! Bit of a dark horse there. Went off with Mrs Gillespie. Joined the Sunderland Division. Didn't you hear – her being your next door neighbour and all?'

The man doffs his Sally Army cap and smiles at Margaret.

'Fancy shoes, Missus,' he says. 'Off somewhere nice then?'

*This originally came from an observation made by a woman at St Mary's Church coffee morning when she told of a man who used to sing in the streets for money. This made me think about the loneliness of it and the need for something beautiful in people's lives.*

# Lightening Lass

## Chris Robinson

The clock chimed out from the dining room below, waking me from a pleasant dream. I counted the gongs as I rubbed sleep from my tired eyes. I counted eight in total. I allowed time to get used to the sunlight that filled the room through the thin, faded curtains.

I sat up in bed, my feet feeling around the cold lino flooring for my slippers. I washed and dressed before heading down the creaking stairs through the living room to the back of the house. Dad was sitting at the dining room table with his racing pages and betting slips in hand. Mam stood over a hot skillet in the kitchen. The smell of bacon sizzling in the pan was making my mouth water.

'Get yourself a glass of juice and sit up at the table, breakfast's almost ready.' Mam spoke without looking up from the pan. I did as she said, sitting down opposite Dad with my glass of juice. I spotted John out of the corner of my eye. He was in the garden cleaning out the kennels. I heard the clinking of crockery as breakfast was plated up. 'Kate, call your brother in.'

I promptly unhooked the latch from the single-paned window and pushed it ajar and called out 'John, breakfast!'

We ate in silence as always, then John went back to his duties outside while I helped Mam with the washing up. By nine thirty everything was cleared away and I sat in the chair by the telly with my feet dangling over one of the chair's arms. Mam was on the couch with a book in hand.

Dad poked his head round the dining room door. 'We're off to the track pet. We'll be back in time for tea. Don't forget to take those slips for the bookies will you? I've left them on the sideboard with the money.'

Dad had raced greyhounds since I could remember. He and John were taking Bess to the village track for the first time. Our Lucy had to stay home. She was too old to race now and was enjoying her retirement.

At eleven o'clock Mam and I walked to the colliery to do the errands. We visited the library to return the old books and to choose some new ones. Then we called at the bookies to place Dad's bets. We picked up a link of pork and beef sausages for tea and a joint of brisket for Sunday lunch from the butchers, and bought some fresh rolls from the bakers. I helped Mam pick out vegetables from the greengrocers and she gave me ten pence to buy a mix up. By the time she had finished talking to Mrs Box I'd eaten the whole bag.

We made our way back up Seaside Lane towards home, Mam called out greetings now and again to neighbours who passed by. I helped put the groceries away and Mam made sandwiches for lunch. I was allowed out to play after that. I found my friend Helen sitting in her garden and asked if she wanted to come out to play. We ran and hopped and skipped and ended up a while later along Petwell Lane.

'I'm going to pick flowers for my mam,' Helen said.

I'd decided to make perfume with the petals of the flowers I picked. When our hands were full we started to make our way home.

'What's that noise?' Helen asked, stopping in her tracks.

'What noise?' I asked.

Helen shushed me and we both stood very still, our ears straining to hear a faint scuffling sound. It sounded like something was coming along the track. Not a car or a farm vehicle, it was far too quiet, but it seemed to be coming towards us at lightening speed.

Helen had turned and started to run away but my legs were like jelly and I couldn't move. I screamed as a figure bolted around the corner and right into my path. I fell and the figure fell with me. The flowers from my hand scattered along the gravel. I was now on my back and I was aware of a smelly hot wet tongue licking at my face. I could hear Helen laughing from somewhere behind and my horror turned to relief as I took hold of Bess's collar and got to my feet.

'How in the world did you get here lass and where've you left Dad and John?'

Of course Bess couldn't answer, so Helen and I walked a way up the lane but couldn't find Dad or John anywhere so we decided to take Bess home. Helen took her Mam the flowers she had picked before they wilted. When I got home Mam was preparing the tea. She looked surprised to see Bess with me. 'Is your Dad and John with you?' she asked.

'No Mam.' I replied and explained what had happened.

Mam asked me to put Bess in her kennel and help with the tea. Dad and John arrived home a little later looking flustered.

'Get washed up, tea will be ready soon.' Mam said.

'No time for tea, pet, I have to go back out and look for our Bess. She took off as soon as we let her loose on the track. We've spent hours looking for her.'

Without looking up Mam calmly said, 'Bess is in her kennel.'

Dad and John both looked at each other then out of the kitchen window and sure enough there she was.

'But how..?' Dad was too lost for words.

'Our Kate found her and brought her home.'

Dad looked at me and, smiling broadly, I nodded, 'She came at me like lightening she did.'

Dad stood in thought for a moment then said, 'Well then, that's what I'll call her, Lightening Lass.'

We all sat down to sausages, egg and chips and I got to tell my tale of how I rescued Bess and brought her home.

# Fens' World

## Mavis Farrell

We are the Fens
Both girls and boys
We love each other

We walk our own walk
Talk our own talk
Hate our own hates
Like our own likes
Need our own needs
And fear
Our own fears.

We fear
Druggies smack heads and perverts.

They shout
And give us
Dirty looks
And say we owe the dealer
Thirty quid.
That isn't true
Cause we aren't druggies.
We are scared
To walk alone
And we run away.

We don't have
A swimming pool with a slide
McDonalds or
Cinema or decent shops
Or things to do,
Like a carnival
Or a bike track.

We don't like
Disgusting littered streets
Needles on the stony beach
Shops all closed
And ruined
People drinking too much.

We like best
Ourselves.
Our other Fens
Our mams
Our families
Our school - sometimes.
The library
The parks
But Horden Park is the best
In the whole world.

What we need is
More fun
More sun
More police to chase
The smack heads.
Knock the colliery houses down
And the old school
We need more space
Then we will have
The best place
Ever.

*This poem was written following an interview with girls aged between five and thirteen years in Easington library. They call themselves Fens which in their language means friends. Using their words, this poem presents a refreshingly candid view of life for young people in Easington today, demonstrating their understanding of the problems faced and the possible solutions.*

Mavis Farrell

# City Slicker

Agnes Frain

Something was up. No idea what, but it's a puzzle, My oldest brother Conner is in the frame.

Since his return from Sheffield, where he and a group of mechanics had been on an intense training course, he seemed content to sit with the family most evenings. OK, his pals collect in our home as usual. The noisy good-natured mayhem remains. But? Where are the pretty girls? He always had a girl in tow who flutters her eyelashes and acts coy while we younger siblings giggled behind her back.

Something was different now.

Running home from school, I was surprised to see my parents busy removing the dining room wallpaper. Ordered to peel the vegetables with the hindrance of my twin sisters, I tried to remember when the paper was last removed. For as long as I could recollect mum changed the downstairs paper every two years. It wasn't two years since the last chaos.

When I questioned it, I was told, "Curiosity killed the cat." Well there can't be many people in our street with curiosity, there's loads of cats hanging about.

Now the dining room looks posh. With the aid of my dad and his ruler the paper has fancy corners with a dip in the middle: very classy. No doubt, our street would be awash with dipped corners as nosey neighbours popped in for a peep.

Now the sitting room is being attacked. Scrape, scrape, the noise sets my teeth on edge. Music from the radiogram: we kids watch as my sister Tess dances around the room with her boyfriend. Conner shouts, one two *three*, one two *three*, turn and slide. When did *he* learn to dance? He claims he had two left feet. I know he's lying. They look normal to me.

Apart from my parents and Conner we've spent the day on the beach, the sun is hot but the sea as usual is cold. Only the brave venture further than their knees into the water. Then a sneaky unexpected wave washes over us. Screams of shock echo along the shore. We struggle out of the foam: our hand-knitted swimsuits sag with water. It streams down our legs. Tess and her pal Hetty roll around the sand as they shriek with laughter. Very funny! It's unfair. They have elasticised suits and bathing caps.

We're tired and hungry when we open the kitchen door. Mum stands like a sentry against it. We're hustled into the kitchenette and ordered into the bath, one by one. We're scrubbed then put in our nightclothes. Then at last, we're allowed into the dining room.

A beaming Tess and Conner stand back. Instead of our battered familiar scrubbed topped table and assorted chairs, there - gleaming in the fire light - stands a long polished table with eight matching chairs. Against the wall, the old press is missing; in its place is a small sideboard.

Before we even have a chance to stroke the smooth, unmarked wood it is covered with a heavy piece of felt. Sitting primly on the chairs with strict orders not to kick the furniture we at last eat our tea.

In the next few days, every time we return from school something has changed. Two plush rocking chairs with a couch appear. They are shrouded in old sheets to keep them clean. Mum isn't a fussy mum so why is she worried about furniture being spotless? Gone is the lovely patterned clippie mat. We all spent spare minutes working on that beauty. Instead a plain rug lies in front of the hearth.

I begin to get nervous, was it our turn next. Were we about to be replaced by children with blonde curls and wide smiles?

The summer holidays arrive and weeks of bliss lie ahead. The sun is hot and the crack of cricket balls, followed by enthusiastic applause, draws kids likes magic. They will slip in between adults then swarm around the boundaries, desperate for a touch of the ball.

Conner is running about with a big grin on his handsome face. He's togged out in his best suit. I watch as - with the aid of two brushes - he slicks his thick black hair into a neat style.

He winks at me then checks to see if his teeth are clean. He's really vain. He looks at his watch then sails out. I follow him, and then spy around the corner as he leaps onto a bus that will take him to Durham.

Mum has removed her apron. This is a first; it never comes off till we are ready for bed. Even more of a shock! Dad is home from the allotment. Before tea, in the early afternoon! Hours of digging time lost. Tess is busy as she hunts for invisible dust.

We younger ones are dragged to the sink, loud protests from my brothers about their second wash of the day. Mum scrubs us with a face-cloth then, with threats to keep clean, she ousts us into the back lane.

The answer to the puzzle is now clear; someone from the big city is on a journey to our village. I try to remember geography lessons. Sheffield is a steel city with dozens of iron works. Our cutlery is engraved, *Made in Sheffield.* Good. At least I won't look too dumb.

I gallop back to the bus stop, desperate to get the first glimpse of this stranger. In the distance, I can see the bus; overcome with shyness I duck into the catholic schoolyard and peer through the iron railings.

My brother strolls past. There, arm linked through Conner's, was a vision - dark curly hair and a smiling, red painted mouth and lovely clothes. She looks like a film star. Conner is toting her enormous case. He looks at ease but he doesn't fool me. His shoulders are at that angle.

I dawdle after them; the contrast between this alien and our pit village is miles apart. I speed down the back lane to join my sisters and brothers who have not moved from the yard gate. Full of importance I whisper to them that the visitor is a young woman and she looks like a film star.

Voices drift across. Liam, who can see over the gate, ducks down and speaks in an exaggerated whisper, 'She's smoking a cigarette!'

Well, apart from our dad nobody in our family smokes, not in front of our parents they don't. So! She's one of those sophisticated girls who blows smoke and looks mysterious, like Bette Davis.

And our Tess, what are her thoughts? Tess is gentle and pretty but, like most of the young girls in our village, her outfits were sensible - made to last. This girl must be rich; her clothes are sleek and glamorous.

We wander inside, intermittently afraid we will frighten our visitor away if we run in a mass. We're greeted with a smile and a shake of hands. This is a change as we kids are usually banished when we have company.

Above her lips was a beauty spot - not a painted one, a real beauty spot. Our guest was not stuck behind a door when looks were given out. (I heard my Gran make this cruel remark about a plain plump girl with spots who had been 'behind a door.')

Our visitor is called Poppy. She speaks in a husky voice and calls us 'love'. The males of the family are awe-struck. Conner, puffed up with pride, informs us kids he met Poppy at ballroom classes. Bored after college work he and his pals decided they would learn to dance. Poppy was one of the instructors.

Later I spot Tess run a comb through her glossy dark hair then pull her blouse straight. My lovely sister, like the rest of us, feels drab and old fashioned.

As the holiday progresses we relax, our games of cards and dominoes resume. Poppy slaps down her cards with gusto, eyes sparkling with enjoyment. We discover she works in a cutlery factory. She presents mum with some pearl-handed fish knives, bought from the staff shop. Mum is delighted but we all know they'll be unused. They will join the other treasures tucked away in the sideboard.

Poppy explains about Master Cutlers, who are very skilled. She is describing a foreign world. We live in the sound of pitmen's boots, the pit buzzer's blare, cobbled streets and the clank of the winding wheel.

Every day a new outfit appears from her case, wrapped carefully in tissue paper. That case is an Aladdin's cave. We had one wardrobe in our bedroom, shared by four girls. Poppy must have a spare room. Our house is always crowded, I feel sorry for her. She must be lonely.

Neighbours pop in to view the star. Most of the woman wear wrap-around aprons to preserve their scant wardrobes. They stroke the material of Poppy's dresses, laughing at the idea of themselves ever wearing such finery.

Overhearing a conversation between Tess and our visitor I hear the word 'dressmaker.' It dawns on me that her mum is a seamstress. She designs and sews Poppy's numerous outfits. So, not only is Poppy pretty and kind, but she has her own personal dress designer. Some people have all the luck!

The holidays are nearly over but before Poppy returns home, she and Conner plan a trip to see Sunderland play with a bunch of friends. All the girls - Tess included - wear sensible flat shoes and jackets. They know standing shoulder to shoulder, swaying with an excitable crowd, is hard on the feet. Tough men clad in heavy boots aren't always considerate.

Off the group trot up the cobbled lane to catch the bus. Poppy wears a matching pink brocade dress and coat. Women outside their gates, gossiping, smile as the city slicker, band-box perfection, sends up a tattoo on the hard cobbles with her six inch heeled navy shoes.

# My Moon

Mary N. Bell

When I was a child
The man in the moon
Looked down and smiled
With a round kind face
Made of cream cheese
He chopped sticks and glowed
I was safe and at ease
When the full moon shone down on me.

In August July and June
Any month of the year
I could rely on the moon
To set romance astir
Beaming a silvery dream path
Rippling on sea to land
As I strolled along the shore
With my lover hand in hand.

A crescent then a quarter
Whole half then full moon
He'd watch see and never tell
Of how he cast a spell
So that a special he
Would think romantically
And fall for my beguiling charms
And long to hold me in his arms.

Then all my dreams were spoiled
Astronauts landed
Walked on my moon's face
As though an ordinary place
Talked of dust rocks and a crater
My moon- computerised data
No longer can lovers croon or spoon
What have they done to my moon?

They think they've ruined my moon
But we have an affinity
From the midnight starry sky
He looks down and winks his eye
He shines down as he's always done
So my lover and I still have fun
From early July till late June
Under my magical mysterious moon.

# The Outsider

Ann Peel

The council gardeners mowed the grass of the empty house and workmen were inside doing minor repairs. It was going to happen, Susie thought, there had been no one else to view it. The man would soon be moving in, she wondered what his family were like. Terry wasn't too interested, 'As long as they keep the place decent, I won't complain and maybe I'll have a new drinking mate,' he said.

Two weeks later the council came again, bringing their standard furniture for a furnished let. By the time Terry got in from work it was the talk of the street. Susie told Margaret, who told Barbara, who told Jean and so it went on. Terry laughed saying that women were gossip mongers and were never happy unless they were miserable. Susie tried to tell him that a single man just would not fit in a family street, especially not a tall good looking one. 'Think of the temptation pet!' said Jean with a smile that made Terry wonder just how tall and good looking this man was.

'You didn't tell me he was good looking!' he responded with a frown. Susie laughed, gave him a flirtatious smile, walked out of the living room and into the kitchen, leaving him quiet and wondering.

On Monday morning, every woman in the street was indoors behind her curtains and watching. No removal van, no furniture, just a couple of battered suitcases and his old Ford Capri - very old, but beautifully cared for, almost in showroom condition and the prettiest, metallic, ice blue colour. As she watched, the man went indoors and closed his curtains. As the morning progressed the girls all met at Barbara's (she was the one with the constant coffee pot). They needed to talk about this.

'He has to be in his late thirties at least,' Barbara commented first.

'I saw a wedding ring,' was Margaret's contribution.

'Maybe he's divorced,' Jean ventured. 'I wonder why?' she added.

'Well, one thing's for sure, he loves his car and isn't very sociable!' Joan's attempt to catch the new neighbour's attention - with a cheery 'Good morning' and her very best smile - received only a sullen 'Morning' in response as he returned to buffing up the already sparkling car.

'I think Terry should be the one to welcome him, find out his name and his story,' Barbara babbled quickly. 'You're his next door neighbours aren't you? Maybe he's just a bit shy with women. Some men are, you know.'

On his first day the new neighbour had already created a stir in the tight-knit street community.

When Terry came home Susie told him of the earlier conversation and he bellowed with laughter. 'You women get me! Think there's something wrong with a feller just because he doesn't give you all of his attention. Thought ever struck you he's just settling in?' He paused. 'I'll wait till the weekend and ask him to come for a drink with the lads, OK?'

End of conversation. Susie knew there was no point pushing him.

All that week the women waited, watching as the man went shopping, polished his car and stayed home. Their conversations centred around this quiet man who, although they all tried to be friendly, just did not respond, not even a smile. On Friday Stephen's football hit the bonnet of the man's car. Susie held her breath as he came out to the gate. She saw Stephen apologise, and you could tell the man was talking to her boy. She went to the front door and called, 'Stephen, tea's ready!'

Stephen said goodbye to the man and ran indoors.

In the house a confused Stephen asked, 'Where's me tea, mam?'

'Not yet pet. I just thought you might be in trouble over the ball hitting the car?'

Stephen smiled, 'Oh no, he was fine about it. Just said I should be a bit more careful, it's worth a lot of money you know, mam.'

'What is?'

'The car of course, what did you think?'

'David says I should try for the local junior team. He said he'd been watching me play all week.'

'David, who's David?' Susie was now also confused.

'Mister Next Door of course. What's up, mam? You sound upset.'

'Nothing pet. I'm just a bit tired, that's all.' But her mind was working overtime. Doesn't respond to women. Not bothered with anyone really until this thing. And he thinks the world of that car and it's worth a lot of money. So why didn't he shout and bawl like the other men did if you endangered their precious things? All this tumbling around in her head but she continued preparing tea. She sent Stephen to wash his hands. How come only a 9 year old boy learns his name? She shuddered at what she was thinking. Then she shook her head and told herself not to be silly, Terry would ask him for a drink and everything would be fine. End of!

Terry came in from work, ate and went to change for his night with the lads. He came downstairs in his shirt and tie looking for all the world like he did when they first met. Was it really twelve years ago? She really did love him.

He smiled. 'I'm just gonna call next door, see if whatsisname wants to come.'

'David. That's his name.' she said.

'So, he told you his name?'

'No, he told Stephen.' Susie explained what had happened earlier.

'Good, I won't feel such a Charlie then. I can make an apology for an excuse eh?' Off he went, smiling and whistling to knock on the man's front door.

Susie sat in her armchair, waiting and wondering. When he came back he looked a little bemused. 'What's wrong?' she asked.

'Well, the feller doesn't drink! So I said come and have a Coke with us then. But he still said no. I wonder if he's just broke and too embarrassed to say. Well, maybe another time eh?'

After Terry had gone to find his cronies, Susie sat and looked at television. But she wasn't really watching it; her mind was running like a loop tape at the club!

On Saturday morning at Barbara's, Susie looking out of the window, saw Stephen playing in the front garden, letting Susan keep goal for him. Then she saw the man come to the adjoining fence; the children stopped playing and started to talk to the man. They laughed like they had been friends for years.

'Why the long face Susie?' Margaret asked.

'I was just watching the kids talking to that David next door.'

'David, is that his name?' came a chorus of three.

'Did he actually speak to you?' grinned Barbara.

'No, he's spoken to Stephen and now to Susan. Seems he only talks to kids and he doesn't drink. He turned Terry down for a night at the Buffs.' The words careened out of her mouth and her friends were shocked.

'Whatever is wrong, Susie, this isn't like you?' said Margaret.

'I don't know. It just worries me - a man on his own, won't look at women, won't go out with the lads. But he talks to children like they are his best friends. She paused. 'Don't they have to tell you when a paedophile is in your street?'

'Where did all that come from?'

Susie was ashamed of herself, she had put into words what had been running through her mind all night. 'Sorry girls. I didn't get much sleep last night. Forget what I said. I'm just going to have a lie down. Bye!' Off she went, across the road, calling the children to come indoors, now!

'What were you talking to *him* about?' she asked the children as calmly as she could.

'Oh just football and school and favourite subjects,' said Susan.

'You know, all the things grown-ups always ask,' said Stephen.

'Well keep out of his way. Don't make a nuisance of yourselves. Okay?'

'Alright Mam, don't worry, we won't'.

But she did worry. 'Wonder where he works. Has he got the week off? Will he go back to work tomorrow? Hope so! This is silly. I mustn't tell Terry, he'll think I'm going *doolaly.*'

Tuesday morning, at coffee at Barbara's, she noticed the others watching out of the window. She asked them what was wrong. Barbara said 'That David worries me too. He was watching our children with a hungry look on his face.' Jean and Margaret nodded in agreement. Susie was really worried now and all four women sat brooding with their coffee getting cold. Eventually Susie said that she felt they were worrying about nothing and went home to brood alone.

Later Susie continued with her worrying thoughts. Why did he stay indoors all day Monday, only coming out to tinker with his stupid car when the kids got in from school, letting the boys gather around him to watch and ask questions?

'Well not my Stephen,' she said to herself. 'It finishes tonight. He's staying in!' She started tea and waited for her family to come home. She was right! Four o'clock and there *he* comes to polish his car. Great way to make friends with young boys!'

Terry ushered Susan and Stephen in from school and the boy asked to go and see David's car. 'No! Go and wash your hands ready for tea.'

'Oh dear that was too stern,' she thought and Terry looked at her with that keen, *what's going on?* look he had.

Later, when the kids were in bed Terry put his arm around her shoulder and said, 'What's up pet, you seem all on edge?' That was when the floodgate broke and her fears tumbled out fast and furious. Not only what she thought but what the others had seen. Terry smiled and gave her a quick hug, 'The Council couldn't do a thing like that pet, putting one of *them* in a street full of kids!'

'Is that true though? Wasn't there some talk on the news about not disclosing and an Act of Parliament or something, it's really worrying Terry?'

'I'll look into this tomorrow pet, now don't worry and tell the girls not to worry either.'

But she did, and they did, all watching carefully, both before and after school. One night Terry came home a little later than usual, his face was serious and he told her the Council had refused to answer his enquiries. So he'd rung the police and they were just as adamant. 'Nothing to say on the subject eh?' I said. 'Well that's a sure sign we're right, I'm going over to see the lads, back soon!'

So off he went. Brian went with him to Joe's and they all went to Barbara's house for her husband, Alan. Within minutes the four men, followed by Barbara, Jean, Susie and Margaret all stormed over to David's door and knocked loudly. 'Come on out, you paedo!' they shouted in chorus.

A quavering voice came from inside. 'What do you want? What are you calling me?'

'You're a paedophile and we know it. Come out or we'll smash your car into bits.' Terry shouted.

The door opened a little. 'I don't know what you are talking about, mate, but you have it all wrong, I just want to be left in peace. Now please go away!' He closed the door quickly and the four men threw their combined weight against but it stayed firmly shut. Then, picking up anything they could, the men threw missiles of every description at the windows, Margaret and Jean attacked the beloved car, gouging out weals in the lovingly treated paintwork. Susie and Barbara shouted encouragement to the men to keep trying to break the door which gave way at the fourth attempt!

In they all rushed and the man called David was overpowered and punched, kicked, bitten, scratched, attacked with anything to hand. That was when the police arrived! An ambulance was called for the unconscious David; other neighbours and family members were called to take care of the terrified children whose parents had now been arrested. At the station, when questioned, they all insisted that they should have been warned that a paedophile was in their street.

At last the duty Sergeant called a halt to it all by bellowing 'What *paedophile*? There is no paedophile in your street!'

'But that David is, isn't he?' Terry's voice was shocked and muffled by the hand he had put up to his mouth.

The sergeant went on. 'Mr Warren has no police record of any kind. He simply moved to your street because he had nowhere else to go and that's all I can tell you stupid people.' Then the Sergeant put his head down and started on the tedious paperwork to charge these people who had acted first and only now, had started thinking.

Eventually David recovered physically with nothing broken except his heart. His story was that he had come to this place because his wife had informed him that she and their son didn't want him. She'd found someone else who thought more about her than he thought of his car, and would take her for a drink any time she wanted. David knew that he'd have to bide his time and find a home if he and his son were ever to be together again.

He had posted a letter soon on the day he arrived in the new house. He had the answer now. His son's reply was in his pocket. '*Make it soon Dad please, I miss you, love James.*'

He decided that now he'd have to try again somewhere else. He vowed that this time he'd speak to nobody, not even the children.

# Bevin Boys

## Mary N. Bell

1943. He wanted to be a fighter pilot. As soon as he was eighteen he volunteered for the Royal Air Force. He couldn't wait for his call up papers. To get into R.A.F uniform and fight for his country was his ambition. He had a place at university but that was put on hold for the duration however long it took to win this war.

Then a letter arrived, telling him he was being drafted into the coalmines to be a Bevin Boy – so called after the politician who invented the role to make up for the shortage of labour. The numbers 0 to 9 were placed in a hat, a number was pulled out and if your National Service number had this number in, it was the pits for you. John was called up to be a Bevin Boy. He protested in vain. A refusal to obey orders meant imprisonment. John had no choice. No glamorous uniform for him.

Although used to living in rural Devon he was soon on his way to The Training Centre, Horden, County Durham, a pit village on the bleak North East coast. There he was kitted out with a safety helmet, boots and an overall. He had been instructed to take some old clothes with him as, when he left Horden, the overalls would be taken from him. When his four week training was finished he was sent to another pit to begin his life as a miner.

As a Devon boy, John had not realised how picturesque this part of the coast was. Wartime restrictions meant locals were forbidden to go to the beach but John could not resist a visit and was awed at the vastness of the whole coast - the sea pounding up the beach and the awesome sight of waste from down the pit being thrown into the sea by an aerial flight turning the beach black He had known where coal came from but never thought much about it, till now. He had never thought about the pit conditions or the polluted air breathed in down below.

His first experience of going down the pit was hair raising. Approaching the pit cage, appropriately called as they were crammed in and fastened in, a strange smell came from the clothes of the experienced miners. He heard a bell ring then felt the woosh as the cage dropped down hundreds of feet to the bowels of the earth in a flash. His ears popped. A man told him to take deep breaths. John's last night's supper met this morning's breakfast. At the bottom of the shaft he staggered out of the cage and was taken *in-bye* to where he was to work.

The smell was overpowering. Human waste mixed with pit ponies droppings and the dank, damp putrid smell made him retch. No good holding his breath. He would be down here for seven hours or so. No toilets down here, no bathroom facilities, go where you could and eat your bait with germ-laden hands! John never got used to any of this, but came to admire the miners whom he never was to forget.

In his free time he went to the local Working Men's Club. He was there one night when a fight broke out between a young man called Tommy and and an older man called Bobby. The older man did not defend himself. Their marras (workmates) were on hand to hold the younger man back. A baby was mentioned.

John kept out of it and asked no questions.

The next day at work he recognised both of the men who had been involved in the scrap. They worked near each other but did not speak. Then there was a rumbling noise followed by shouting, and a louder noise still. Then silence. All John could hear was the pit patter of odd bits of coal falling from the caved-in roof. There had been a fall of stone and coal, the dread of every miner.

Even before the dust cleared they were shouting, are you there? and calling out names. Who was missing? Bobby. The first man to the rescue? Tommy. He dug frantically with bare hands until he had freed the buried man's head and then went on digging, 'Dad, dad!' he said. 'Sorry, sorry, sorry'. With the help of his marras and John they got him out and stretchered him to the shaft bottom.

Tommy never left his father's side. Bobby did recover after many weeks.

Curiosity got the better of him. John asked one of his workmates what it was all about.

'Well it's like this, son,' the man said. 'Tommy's 24. His Da Bobby's 48. Bobby's wife, the lad's mother, is gannin' to have a baby. When Tommy was told this, he went light. Called his own Da a dirty old man! They've been married 25 years. I'd say they're only young. Tommy thinks they are too old for that kind of thing so he left home and every time he sees his Da he gans off it and lashes out.'

A storm in a teacup, John thought. My parents are their age. How would I feel? Don't go down that path.

In the end the accident did bring father and son together. By the time the war ended and John left the pit to go back to normality he saw Tommy walking along happily and proudly with his own pregnant wife and a toddler, his little sister.

John was to say later, 'My experience at Horden taught me to have great respect and admiration for miners, so much so that as a member of the Bevin Boys' Association I am campaigning with them for a National Miners' Day. For years we thought of ourselves to be "The Forgotten Army" as through no fault of ours we became Bevin Boys. After many years of campaigning to be recognised we learned recently that we are entitled to three medals for war service. On the 60th anniversary of WW2 we were allowed to join with the armed forces to carry our green banner down the Mall on Remembrance Day. Our uniform – pit helmets. We placed our wreath with pride in remembrance of comrades lost during the war, not forgetting the unsung heroes who died in the darkness of the mines.

*Ernest Bevin, Minister of Labour, found that a shortage of coal would prolong the war. What to do?*
*Ask all miners who had been conscripted to return to the pits? Unfortunately not enough of them wanted to*
*return so Bevin, with the War Office, decided to have men conscripted to the pits. What to call them?*
*Could they be called an army? They became known as Bevin Boys.*

# George

Susan Robinson

'This is me,' he said, as he showed his photograph
'Nowt but a lad, and my dog, of course - Rex
I thought I was a man then,
With my long legs
And a wage coming in because
I worked at the pit.
My mam said to wear my suit for the picture
But I'd grown since it was bought for my dad's burying
So it didn't fit, anymore.
It was the pit that killed him - black lung
And we put him in the ground that he'd spent his life
Trying to dig out.

I hated fancy clothes and shiny shoes.
Why, man, I always got wrong mucking them up
But, for the photograph,
And to please my mam
I slicked back my hair and wore my cap.
I took the funeral suit off afterwards and threw it back of the cupboard
I just knew she'd have a fit.
I can hear her now
"There's life in them clothes yet, George," she said
"Aye, but not my life," I said back
No dapper look for me.
No prancing nancy suit to fasten me tight.

I took the dog and stuffed the ferret in my pocket
And did away over the fields
Past Paradise.
Walking in the outdoors above the ground
Was always what I wanted
Catching rabbits
With ferret and net
A humpty-backed pie for my dinner
Looking for hares at the end of the day,
Jinxing and boxing
In golden dust-moted air -
A sight that would still gladden my heart.

Susan Robinson

Better than the pit -
That black hole that drains away life
That underground warren of narrow roads grey with dust,
Tracked by booted feet and iron rails
Seven South, Fourth North,
Low Main and Hutton Seam
High Main and The Duckbills
Accompanied by a silent wind that speeds between dark stalactites
Hanging from propped canopies of rock
Bringing noise of toil.
Man, machine, pony,
Hollow. Heavy. Deep.

You carried the smell of the pit to the top,
A smell that's all its own
That clung to your clothes and hair
A smell that you tasted at home
Blue marks from falling rock tattooed on skin,
Like prisoners.
Coal dust hung in air -
Silver slivers that threatened breath
And many days weren't light at all, just black night
But my mam had no-one else
Ten years of the pit rusted memories and dreams
Of outdoor life, high skies and distant hills.

Then there was Ruth, my bonny lass
I fell for her proper,
My insides tossed about
Like going fast
In the cage down the pit shaft
And it didn't matter so much that I'd become coal's slave,
And buried my need to walk above the earth.
But the babby's birth took them both and I sank into a pit
Deeper than the mine.
Black despair that smothers, thick like coal dust,
Heavy as fire damp,
I hadn't seen that explosion coming.

I decided then to leave behind the stench and darkness of the mine
And become a wanderer, with no fixed abode
And tramp my life away in green-mossed lanes,
Tracked with prints of hare, rabbit, fox,
Petwell Loren, Blind Lane, Hawthorn Hythe, Andrew's Hill.
I'd taste the smell of sharp cut grass
And listen to the song of birds
Breathe clean air of open fields under rain-washed canopies of trees
In winds that might blow cobwebs out
Or caress a weathered cheek
And sleep with stars, but not alone
A dog beside me, still.

But as you see I'm here in Ashwood Park, canny as care homes go,
I'm getting on now but clean and fed
They shaved the whiskers burnt the clothes
My dog had died a while before
I'd buried him at the three streams down Hawthorn Dene.
And nowadays my body sits and never leaves
This code-locked place
Arthritis and a stroke.
But in my mind I walk with Rex
The unfettered boundaries of my life
And take myself off - over fields,
Towards Paradise.

Susan Robinson

F. Naughton

83

# A Quiet Night In

## Terry Dobson

The girls giggle as they sit around the table and the makeshift Ouija board. Candles flicker on the fireplace casting eerie shadows around the dimly-lit room.

'Come on, fingers on the glass,' Tanya said.

It is Tanya's parent's house, so she naturally takes charge. Her parents are out for the evening at the Colliery Club, so they have the house to themselves.

The girls place their index fingers on the glass in the centre of the table.

'Is there anybody there?' says Tanya in a put-on quavering voice. '*Is there anybody there?*'

Another shared giggle. Then the glass moves slowly at first, then speeds up and touches the piece of paper with 'Yes' written on it. The girls squeal.

'You pushed that!' Julie says to Tanya.

'I didn't! Honest!' Tanya, indignant, replies.

'Who are *you*?' Tanya asks, this time a bit shakily.

The glass moves left to touch the letter S, then quickly across to the right for the A, and then to the M. Then it stops.

'Sam? Is your name Sam?' Tanya asks.

The response comes quickly, 'Yes'.

Tanya then notices that Jackie has taken her finger off the glass and is hiding her face, which seems pale. She's shaking.

'Jax, what's wrong?' Tanya asks.

Jackie shakes her head and draws in a deep breath. 'I-I had a brother called Sam, but he died when he was a baby,' she says trembling.

Tanya stares at Jackie in shock for a moment. She looks down at the glass.

'Are you Jackie's brother?' she asks hesitantly.

'No,' comes the reply.

Tanya thinks for a moment. 'Sam could be either a boy's or girl's name. Are you a boy?'

The glass slides to touch the paper marked 'No.'

'So you're a girl?' Tanya asks.

Once again there is a negative response.

The girls look at one another.

'Are you human?' Tanya asks.

The glass seems to take on a life of its own, moving so quickly that the girls almost lose touch with it. 'No!' comes again.

'An animal?'

The glass indicates 'Yes.'

Tanya thinks for a moment. 'Are you a cat?'

Once again the answer is an emphatic 'No!'

'A dog?'

At this the candle flames suddenly seem to stretch upward for about three feet, making the room seem a lot brighter. Then a gust of air blows them out. The glass flies from the table and smashes against the wall. The girls scream in terror, jump up, knock down chairs in their haste, and huddle together for comfort. Their hearts thump, their mouths are dry, and they shiver and cry.

They cling together for what seems like hours, but is only about ten minutes. Everything is quiet, very quiet. They calm down a little. Tanya slowly stands and slides her hand along the wall until she finds the light switch. She flicks it on, and to the girls' relief there is light at last.

'Let's not do that again!' says Tanya. The others nod and agree emphatically.

Jackie has to go home. The others are sleeping over with Tanya.

Putting on her coat Jackie walks to the door, saying goodbye to everyone. Opening the door, she hears a vicious growl. Looking down on her is a huge black dog, teeth bared, drool dripping from its jaws. She screams.

# Dodging Dora

## Joan Wright

Fred Fawcett had long wearied of his wife Sally's constant moaning about Dora Fenton, two doors along.

Dora was a sixty-something, beady-eyed, better-to-avoid type of person and the majority of her neighbours did indeed keep their distance. However, she had once coerced kind-hearted Sally into shopping for her ('it's my poor old legs') and, months later, Sally was still shopping for the two of them three times a week, Mondays, Wednesdays and Thursdays.

She did her best trying to avoid her, varying the times of day, but to no avail. 'She always catches me, sometimes with a shopping list as long as her arm,' she'd wail to Fred. 'If I could dodge her, just once, I'd be a very happy woman.'

Fred was also a kind-hearted soul who cleaned Ellie Trott's wheelie-bin once a fortnight. His reward was a delicious home-baked apple pie.

It was late Wednesday afternoon and he'd just finished cleaning the bin. He gave it a final squirt of disinfectant and closed the lid. Sally was in the house sulking after he'd told her to 'belt up' about Dora. 'Just tell the bloody woman you can't do her shopping any more. It's as simple as that.'

He'd soon felt contrite and, while cleaning the bin, figured out a way she could avoid Dora – for once any way. 'It would make my day as well,' he chuckled to himself, 'but getting the old girl to agree might prove difficult. Still, she can be persuaded.' As he walked through the door he called out to her. 'Hey, pet, I know how you can dodge Dora tomorrow. It's foolproof; I bet you ten quid.'

Thursday morning was reasonably warm and Fred was in the garden, carefully placing Ellie's wheelie-bin on its side. Sally stood in the doorway, shopping bag in hand, telling herself that she was worse than mad to have agreed to such a stupid plan. She'd finally consented after Fred, determined to get her to yield, promised her £50 – win or lose.

Fred went to the open gate and looked up and down the street. It was almost eight o'clock and no one was about. He turned and beckoned to Sally then went to the bin and lifted the lid. 'Come on lass, jump ... or rather crawl to it,' he urged, savouring every moment.

'Get lost,' she said huffily, walking towards it. 'I'll crawl inside when I'm there, not before. I still have some pride.'

Fred, now really keyed up, bowed as five-feet-and-a-bit Sally, bordering on plump, got down on all fours and began crawling into the bin.

'Other way round, woman, other way round,' Fred hissed, giving her a light smack on her protruding posterior.

Sally dutifully turned around and crawled in backwards, telling him to 'keep his hands to himself, thank you very much' and muttering what a right prat she felt. Fred, grinning broadly, pushed her shopping bag down the side and asked if she was comfortable enough. She just glared at him.

'In a few minutes time, love, you'll be sitting in Ellie's, cock-a-hoop that you've dodged Dora and will, tomorrow morning, be fifty pounds into pocket.' He raised his eyes heavenwards. 'Bloody fifty pounds,' he thought. 'My throat's going to be as dry as Jonty Brown's humour.'

Fred pushed the bin into the path and through the open gate. He began wheeling it along the street. 'I'll have to tell her to spend the fifty quid on slimming classes,' he thought. 'She's quite a hefty load.'

He got safely past Dora's and as far as Cissy Swift's gate when the lid opened slightly. 'Go back! I've left my purse on the table; we'll have to go back.' Sally's voice was a mixture of panic and despair.

'You've what? Blast, blast, blast!' Fred thumped the lid in frustration and gave a long drawn-out sigh. 'I'll go back; you stay very quiet and keep the lid shut. No peeking mind; I'll only be a few ticks.'

He was hurrying back just as Cissy opened her door. She immediately spotted the bin. 'Oh good, they've delivered my new wheelie.' She walked to the gate. 'They could have wheeled it in though,' she muttered. 'Well, Jed can do that when the lazy blighter gets out of bed. I'll put the ashes and the peelings in though.'

Cissy went to the back door and picked up a pail containing the previous two days' peelings and ashes. She was returning to the bin when she spotted two policemen on the opposite side of the street. They were walking slowly along, one behind the other, looking carefully in each garden. Her gaze firmly fixed on them, she opened the lid and haphazardly emptied the pail's contents without even a cursory glance inside. She didn't notice the bin's slight wobble as the garbage cascaded over the hapless Sally, or hear a croaking 'Bloody hell' as she slammed down the lid. Cissy went to the back door, left the pail, and went inside. She went up the stairs, into the bedroom, walked over to the bed and prodded a snoring Jed.

'There's two policemen in the street,' she bawled. Jed, lying on his back, mouth wide open, continued snoring. 'What a revolting sight,' she wailed. 'And to think I could have married Joe Preston!'

Alice, next door, looking out of the window noticed Cissy putting things in the bin. 'She's put it out on the wrong day,' she said to her mother. 'I'll go and sneak some of our rubbish in.' She went into the shed and brought out a black bin bag containing old shoes and slippers, worn-out tights, a couple of old lampshades and two raggy doormats. She carried it outside and, almost bent double, crept along to Cissy's gate. She spotted the policemen who were now at the bottom of their street and hurriedly flung open the lid. She emptied the contents from the bag, slammed the lid shut and scurried home, locking the door. She'd been on the wrong side of the law a few times and, if they came knocking, she wasn't in.

As for Sally, poor thing, she was now wearing a garish, purple lampshade on her head.

Fred came tearing out of the house, Sally's purse wasn't on the table and, after a frantic search, he'd found it behind the telephone. He almost bumped into the policemen. 'Sorry,' he said, obviously watching the officers. He didn't want to give the impression he was running away from them.

'Excuse me,' one of them said and Fred turned. 'You haven't seen a slightly inebriated young woman along here, have you?' She managed to escape from the police car and someone thought they saw her turn into this street.'

Fred shook his head. 'No, sorry,' he said, turning and quickening his pace. He was almost at Cissy's gate when he saw her walk through carrying what looked like a vacuum bag. She lifted the bin lid. 'No Cissy, no!' he yelled. 'That's Ellie's bin.' Too late; the contents were now on top of the lampshade and Cissy was staring disbelievingly inside.

She screamed just as Fred arrived – and the police came running. 'There's something in the bin,' she yelled. 'It's moving. Oh Lord have mercy on us ...and who the hell tipped all this rubbish in?'

The officers arrived and one took hold of the lid. 'I think we've found our young lady, Phil,' he said. 'My, my, I bet you wished you'd stayed in the police car.' The other policeman looked in then swiftly turned around, his shoulders shaking with silent mirth.

'Help me get her out, Phil,' the other said, removing the lampshade. Fred peeked inside and burst out laughing. He just couldn't help it. Sally, almost unrecognisable, was gazing up at him. Her dyed-black hair, now ash-grey and speckled with assorted peelings and her rosy-cheeked face, was covered in ash. A piece of cabbage leaf was sticking out of the corner of her mouth. He slammed down the lid.

'Er ...er ... excuse me, officers, but that isn't the young lady, that's my wife.'

'Sally!' Cissy almost exploded. 'You're joking Fred. What would Sally be doing in **my** wheelie-bin? And don't say you put all this filthy rubbish in as well!'

'It's Ellie's bin. It was a ploy to get one over on Dora 'cos Sally was sick of always shopping for her. In other words, we were dodging her. And it would've worked if Sally hadn't forgotten her purse and I had to go back for it.'

'Oh goodness me, oh hell; I thought the Council had delivered my new bin; it was outside the gate so naturally I assumed it was ... .' Her voice tailed off. 'I didn't put all that rubbish in, though, I swear. I just put in some peelings and ashes and I can't understand it ... I didn't notice Sally when I tipped them in. Why didn't she say something? I certainly would if it had been me in there.' She suddenly began to see the funny side and turned her head away, giggling and saying, 'Poor Sally, stuck in a wheelie-bin, dodging Dora ... and Dora's away for a few days visiting her sick cousin. What a mean trick not letting the poor lass know!'

'WHAT?' Fred's yell could have brought the whole street out – and there were already some interested onlookers. The police officers, side by side, were having a good laugh. 'I haven't been so amused since the mother-in-law got bitten on the backside by her beloved dog,' said Phil.

'Are you absolutely sure this is your wife, sir?' asked the other officer.

'Of course I am,' retorted Fred. He opened the lid. 'Confirm that you're the woman I married, pet, and then I can wheel you home, clean you up and make you a nice cup of tea. Then I'll clean out this bloody bin again while you watch the television.'

'You laughed at me, Fred Fawcett, laughed at me! Lifted the lid up and laughed!' Sally, with some difficulty, stood up. 'Yes officers, I am his wife, I'm very sorry to say – but not for long, mind you, not for long!' She turned her gaze to Fred. 'And the fifty pounds you owe me is now one hundred pounds – fifty for as far as we've got and fifty back again. You and your bloody stupid idea, just to dodge Dora and ...' her voice quivered, 'she's not even here ... she's away ...' she started blubbering. 'It was all for bloody nothing!' She crouched down again, letting the lid fall.

One could almost hear a pin drop. Fred and the police stood silent and Cissy had already scurried into the house. The whole street was silent as if in mourning for Sally's pitiable state.

'Is this the lass you're looking for?' A man appeared at the top of the street, holding on to a struggling mini-skirted girl.

'Yes, yes, keep tight hold of her,' shouted one of the officers. He turned to Fred. 'You've got a packet of trouble for yourself, mister, and no mistake. I bet it's the spare bedroom for you for Lord knows how long.' He shook his head. 'Dodging Dora. She must be a right old so-and-so for you to put the missus in a wheelie-bin just to dodge her. Your mother-in-law, yes, but the missus?' he and his colleague hurried to the top of the street, laughing again.

Fred lifted the lid. 'I agree to the hundred quid, pet,' he said. 'But I still say it was a hell of a good idea. I mean, if Dora hadn't gone away and if you hadn't left your purse behind, you wouldn't have been stuck at Cissy's and ...' A shoe caught him squarely in the face. Sally was standing up again.

'Typical, typical, typical,' she said. 'Blame me and even Dora for going away but not yourself; no, nothing's ever your fault. It's always the same; you never take the blame for anything, never, never, never!' She flung another shoe at him. 'And the bobby's right. It is the spare bedroom for you tonight and I don't know for how long. And before you clean Ellie's bin again you'll have to go and do the shopping because I won't bloody do it, not after the ordeal you've put me through.' Another shoe hit him in the face.

Fred was now a happy man. He knew his canny old missus with her great sense of humour would soon see the funny side and, with a box of her favourite chocolates which he'd bring her from the shops, all would be forgiven. And he'd promise her that he would tell Dora firmly that she would have to do her own shopping in future because it had become too much of a chore for his dear wife. ('It's her legs, y'know'). And he bet himself that he wouldn't be in the spare bedroom that night.

That was a bet he lost.

# Saints and Sinners

## Agnes Frain

'Do you want another cup of tea my dear?' The waitress held the heavy enamel teapot close to her ample chest; she raised her eyebrows and slanted her dark button eyes towards my mum.

Mum, slumped in her seat, her head hung down, turned in my direction seeking guidance. Her eyes were heavy with unshed tears; she was bereft and unable to make even this simple decision. I gently brushed back her thin white hair and wrapped my arm around her bony shoulders then nodded to the waitress.

For a second I thought I saw a flicker of impatience in the hovering woman's eyes, but then she eased the teapot to the edge of the table and resumed her task.

Why the hell did my sister insist on outside catering? Who were these strangers crowded into the small house of my parents? They breathed in precious air, air we needed to sustain us in our grief.

Through the open door I spotted my brother-in-law: as usual he was holding court. With his thick neck his plump well-fed body, his chest stuck out and he stuck his legs apart in his familiar *look at me* pose, he reminded me of a satisfied seal.

An old man was standing near the fireplace leaning on an old stick. His black suit was shiny and smelt as if it had been soaked in mothballs. His rheumy eyes watered and a drip from his nostril was loudly sniffed back. A thin, sharp face and sleek greasy hair topped his scraggy neck. He looked neglected and well- worn.

'Who's that?' I nudged my brother who was busy stuffing his face with the luscious cream cakes. His jowls were working overtime wobbling like a turkey. He swallowed and gulped before answering. 'That's our dad's brother. The last time I saw him was in the early Fifties, before you were born.'

Beside me mum stiffened and raised her head. This was the first time since Dad's sudden death she had looked alive. Her eyes - no longer blank - were like black poisonous pebbles.

'Get him out!' She raised her voice and pointed at him with a shaking finger. 'Get that swine out of my house!' Then she broke into tortuous weeping.

My sister and sister-in-law looked about with mouths agape as they searched for the person who had caused Mum's outrage. My sister fingered her heavy necklace and smoothed down her dress. Even in crisis, her thoughts turned towards her own appearance.

The object of their attention wobbled as he shuffled towards the table. His lips trembled. 'Don't Nell! Don't be like this. He's gone. It's too late for me to apologise but I'm trying to make amends. Just listen for a minute.'

The rattle of dishes in the sink ceased. The clock ticked and in the fire the coal crackled; even the air breathed silently. The silence stretched. We were in a cocoon of thick compressed space. Nobody was willing to chip the breach, to crack the tension.

The chair scraped as mum struggled to her feet and brought us out of our shock. She sobbed; the grief she had stored burst as a dam breaches its walls. Their gnarled hands touched and she held them as if she were clutching a life raft.

Out of the corner of my eye, I glimpsed my avaricious brother-in-law taking advantage of the distraction and slipping dad's medals from the mantelpiece into his pocket.

The rest of us huddled around the table guarding and protecting my mother; we challenged anyone to break the barrier.

Mum snatched her hands away from the intruder's grasp and turned towards the bedroom. My brother, red faced with anger, hooked his arm under the old man's elbow and forced him into the hall and out of the front door. Neighbours and friends began to gather their coats; soon the house was empty of strangers.

I sidled up to my brother-in-law and smiled a wide forced smile. I nodded towards his pocket. 'What a good idea Dan. Mum has wanted the medals mounted for years, but you know dad, never wanted a fuss. Mum will be delighted you've taken the initiative to have them mounted. That'll be a comfort to her.'

Brother-in-law Dan turned puce, his sly eyes shot daggers towards me but I shrugged them off. To rub in my success at besting that toad I patted him on the back as I went in search of mum.

Mum lay on the bed, dry-eyed but chalk white with outrage. She cursed and blasphemed, spitting in her rage. We waited till she'd sunk into a weary silence. Then she began to talk. The bedroom grew dark as she told us the story about our uncle. All the time she spoke, she clung on to our oldest brother.

Her story began when she was fifteen. Our dad and his family were next door neighbours of mum's family; the two families were close, their children played together. In that family Matt was the oldest brother, next in line was our dad and finally Uncle Jack. Matt was the charmer who sweet-talked all the girls and was the star of the street with his curly hair and broad shoulders. 'You should have seen him swagger,' she said. 'He was that confident of himself.'

Then the war came and times were hard. Even then Matt would produce all sorts of extras like magic. He was what they called a spiv, always wheeling and dealing. We celebrated New Year of forty two in style - drink flowed and tears fell, Matt and his next brother, our dad, had received their call up papers.

Mum wiped her eyes and shuddered, 'I was a kid swept away in the moment of loving, Matt took full advantage of me then the next day he disappeared.'

My sister blanched with shame and sniffed away false tears.

'The police hounded his family and so did the army; they pounced on his house day and night in case he was being hidden away. Your dad by this time was in Aldershot doing his basic training. To make things worse the youngest brother Jack sneaked away and joined the navy. He had lied about his age, pleading with his parents not to give him away. Fools that they were they went along with his pretence.'

My brother patted mum's hand and nodded encouragement. 'Go on, mum,' he said.

She went on. 'I realised I was pregnant by that coward. Your grandparents were wonderful. They stood by me.' She looked at my brother who smiled. 'In truth Bob here is uncle's child, he was eight when your dad and I married.'

I was surpised that my brother seemed untouched by this. He held her hand tighter.

She sniffed. 'Anyway, when your dad returned with his terrible injuries I helped his family. They had been devastated by losing young Jack when his ship was shot from the water by U-boats. And had been bewildered by the shame of the way their eldest son had betrayed me and all the family.'

She looked into my eyes. 'Your dad was a hero who fought and survived but he paid a price as you all know. With losing his leg like that, he struggled to find work but still he did what he could. '

I shed a tear now, remembering dad behind his shop counter or sitting on his stool cobbling shoes.

'Then Matt slunk back. Turned out he'd been in prison and it was his turn to scratch a living. He barely looked at his own son. There was no remorse, no tears for his brothers, only a whine of self -pity. He tried to worm his way into your Gran's good books, claiming he wanted to be near his son. I was terrified. He was very persistent.'

That was when mum gave us a radiant smile: her face glowed with love, 'That's when your dad stepped in. He told that snake he was too late. That we had plans to marry and he was going to adopt his nephew.'

I cheered and raised my arm in the air. When I looked round everyone was laughing, even my brother, and I joined in. After we'd stopped laughing she concluded. 'Well, as you know the rest is history. He was a loving father and I was treasured and loved by a good man for a long time, he was my love, my life.' She was smiling. Her misery had been transformed. And we all celebrated the life of our dad the rest of the evening.

# Equi's Ice Cream Shop

Mary N. Bell

Now
Long faces
Hushed silence
Nerves on edge
Waiting room
Mouthwash
Antiseptic
Pain relief

Once
Chatter, laughter
Coffee smells
Ice cream
Bright dresses
Smart suits
Old friends
New ones

Is progress
Happiness?

*Situated in the middle of Seaside Lane, Easington Colliery, this shop was a regular meeting place in the forties and fifties. Many a romance began in Equi's. The pit closed, shops closed and thus Equis became a Dentist's surgery.*

F. Naughton

# The Iron Gates

## Mavis Farrell

The horse stumbled on the rough track rattling the cart from side to side, pitching the woman forward on the hard wooden seat. She clutched the lifeless body of a small boy to her breast. Propped together in a corner of the cart sat two other boys. They looked near death. The gates were opened by an irritable man disturbed from his supper by the clanging of the iron bell.

'Best get the bairns in quick,' grunted the carrier, 'the fever's very bad Bill, very bad.'

'Goodnight and God bless my boys,' said the woman, 'be good for the nurses and say your prayers. Tom, you look after your brothers. I'll be back for you all when the fever's gone and that's a promise.'

She kissed each in turn and sobbed as she gave the little one into the arms of the carrier.

The next day Tom, burning with the fever, winced at the jangle of keys and the clip clop of heels on the wooden floor.

'What have you to report this morning Wilson?'

'The two youngest little brothers from Easington died in the night, but the older one is still with us and putting up a fight, Matron.'

Tom, on hearing this, felt only shame at his failure. He stopped fighting.

Tom was cold to the bone lying on the marble slab. A sickly sweet smell filled the room. He tried to think where he had smelled it before and remembered a dead badger once found in the Dene.

Winter's brown leaves rustled and rattled under the ill-fitting wooden door as a rat sniffed and twitched its way in. Through the strange square window set in the roof, the face of the moon cast Tom a silver glance. His eyes snapped open as he threw off the  transparent sheet. He went to find his brothers.

'Wake up little Alfie, it's time to go.' Tom kissed the icy cheek. Thin arms wound around his neck as he lifted his youngest brother down.

'We've got to find our Joe.'

The boys looked under the sheets but the others were sleeping very soundly, not moving, not waking.

'Box,' pointed Alfie.

There was Joe sleeping the sleep of the dead. They kissed him, tickled him  and blew in his face.

'Come on Joe we'll miss our Mam when she comes for us.'

They watched and they waited. Joe awakened at last as the watery sun rose.

'You always was a good sleeper our Joe.'

Through the pointed arch they found their cut-down clothes and well-cobbled little boots. It was good to get out of the silly white dresses. 'Let's get out lads.'

Looking back over his shoulder, Tom was surprised to see no empty slabs, no disturbed sheets, and the lid was neatly back in place on Joe's box.

Every day the boys walked down the long drive past the pine trees to the iron gates to look for their mother. Their mother never came. People came to read the progress bulletins posted on the gates. Some left food parcels for their loved ones but no one was allowed entry. Thorpe was a fever hospital.

The boys asked everyone about their mother, 'Have you seen our mam, has she come for us?' But no one could see them and no one could hear them. Alfie cried pitifully and Joe cried in anger but their mother never came.

The boys played a lot in the sun, eating from the kitchen if they were hungry and sleeping under the soft blankets at night on a shelf in the clean laundry room. They kept very busy. There was the vegetable patch to tend, hens to feed and rabbits to play with and all the wild birds to watch. The swifts came from Africa in the summer and nested under the eaves of the pavilion wards. Joe wished he could fly away with them too but Tom said, 'No, we must wait for our mother.'

The long years passed, people came and went, but these three little brothers stayed at Thorpe. After the war, fewer people had fevers, instead of sick people women came to have their babies.

New people came every day, patients, doctors, nurses; Tom inspected each new face. During this time he really thought his mother had come.

Tom always did the ward rounds with Matron. He jangled his imaginary keys, peering into all the cots to inspect the babies.

'You've got her off to a T,' Joe said, 'wobbling bum and all.' Then Tom saw his mother! At least he thought so but when he got close he found the sad woman with the empty cot was not his mother at all. He followed her up the path to the nursery where she cried and crooned over a tiny frail baby as transparent as a newly hatched bird.

'Come on baby Tommy. Don't die like my brothers. Get well, be strong, and live,' she said.

Tom knew then that the woman was his baby sister Ellen, all grown up. He was puzzled how this could be.

Tom spent all his days and nights looking after Ellen's baby. He stroked its arms and legs and sang sweet songs when it cried a kitten cry. He tried not to get in the way. The Nursery Nurse slammed the little round window shut. 'We'll have to get this incubator repaired. The door keeps springing open all the time,' she said.

Eventually the baby got better and Ellen took him home. The boys wished they could go too but somehow they couldn't go through the iron gates. They began to sing to the other babies, stroking them to get them to sleep. To make sure each lost one was never forgotten, the boys wove little crosses from iris leaves and stuck them in the bark of the big pine tree near the clinic. They said their prayers for the babies and wished that they could go to Heaven as well but Tom always said, 'We must wait for our mam.'

The boys adopted the staff as their family and loved them all, but Joe tired of his invisibility. He liked an audience so he could show off. Deprived, he became very naughty, his tricks more outrageous and dangerous. He mixed up the Blood Nurse's bottles in the clinic, put salt in Cook's apple pie and unplugged the plugs on the switchboard making the telephonists very flustered.

'This must stop!' said Tom, not often angry. 'Why don't you go and play sword fencing with the pampas grass down by the boiler house and try to be good.'

Joe went too far on the day he tripped up the immaculately-dressed consultant, whom they called the Toff, on his way from the clinic to do his ward rounds. He fell down a deep hole and roared at the workmen. 'Get me out of here at once, don't you know I'm a Consultant?'

'You're just like any other bloke when you're down that hole,' was the workman's reply. The old porter just laughed and Joe rushed off to help him push the dinner wagon.

The night nurses played a game with a circle of papers and a glass in the Doctors' sitting room. The boys helped push the glass. As it started to spell out strange words, the nurses screamed and little Alfie, in excitement, threw a pack of playing cards up in the air where all the hearts and diamonds, clubs and spades slid from the cards and danced around the ceiling, as the bare cards fell to the floor. In that instant, Alfie knew that one nurse could see him. She turned and gave him such a lovely smile that he wished he could go home with her.

The years still passed but the times were not all sad. The boys had such happy days at the Summer Fairs - one of their favourite nurses made lovely toffee, there were cakes and some children came in fancy dress. Once there was football and Joe scored a goal and won the match.

Soon the fun would end. There was talk of closure and despite all the protests, petitions and marches, the hospital did close. Responsibility lay heavily on Tom's narrow shoulders. Where would they go and how could he care for his brothers? Demolition day came. One by one the buildings crashed and fell. The brothers fled from corner to corner, place to place, crouching under hedges in the dust and chaos.

The three boys trudged wearily down the drive to the rusted iron gates, dodging trucks and demolition workers.

'Look,' Alfie pointed, 'there's our nurse, the one who can see us, there she is beside the hedge, under the pine trees. Perhaps she will take us Tom. Perhaps she will take us home?' 'Please take us with you,' begged Tom, but his voice blew away with the roar of the lorries.

The nurse was shouting to them, 'Watch out! Watch that lorry!' Her warning came too late. The lorry drove straight through the boys, but they stood there as before, together, holding hands.

Tom stared in disbelief through the iron gates, his face enraptured, as he pointed to a familiar figure who came towards them from the lane with arms outstretched.

'Mam, I always knew you would come back for us if we waited long enough,' Tom whispered.

They ran to her and she hugged them and kissed them, clutching little Alfie up in her arms. The dust swirled and twirled around them, each mote of dust becoming an incandescent light, making patterns ever changing.

When the dust settled they were gone.

*Thorpe opened as a fever hospital in 1897. The basic huts were replaced by pavilion wards in 1904. Local people suffering from smallpox, diptheria, measles and typhoid were treated in isolation. This self-sufficient community became a much loved Maternity Hospital after the Second World War, finally closing its doors in 1986, prior to demolition. This story is for the Staff who worked there who may have heard the children's laughter and the sound of running feet, they may have felt a breath on the cheek or seen a small shadow in the blink of an eye.*

Mavis Farrell

# A Tongue Twister

## Susan Robinson

The Broth Committee are at loggerheads. They can't agree on how this so-called extra-special broth should be made. Everyone wants to do it her way. *Use bacon bones,* one says. *A nice ham shank,* says another. *I always get a piece of gammon... What about lap of lamb... I like chicken stock... Dice the veg...Grate the carrots and turnip... What? No celery? Let's do dumplings? No it thickens the stock. I don't use barley, just split peas and lentils.* Blah, blah, blah....It's been going on all day.

I'm letting them get on with it. Really I have no choice.

'We're doing this on our own, Bella. You're not taking charge this time, like you always do. We don't need you to show us what we know like the back of our hands. Haven't we all been making broth since we were bairns? It doesn't matter that *we* didn't work at the pit canteen, *or* we didn't help at the strike kitchen making five thousand meals a day.'

It's all gone to their heads. They really want to make an impression. I ask you! At their age? None of them will see sixty five again. It's that bloody *man's* fault. This community centre has always been a woman's domain. Widows and spinsters, all of us. Now *he* turns up and everything's gone bottom up. Figuratively speaking of course.

What a charmer. Why, he's got Gladys all pink and flustered. She's probably never had her hand kissed before by such a smooth-shaven flatterer drenched with Old Spice. It always was *his* favourite aftershave.

Now Ada came out of the caretaker's cupboard with her cardboard hair a mess, shortly after I'd seen him coming out of the same place, mopping his brow with a duster and looking up to no good. Even pikestaff Poll came in wearing red lipstick this morning. Even so it ran into the lines around her mouth and now she looks like Dracula's bride. Sadie's humming 'Sweet Talking Guy' loudly and out of tune. Because she's deaf I expect she thinks no one else can hear.

God, they've all got it badly. That's why they've come up with this idea of a broth and stotty evening for tomorrow night, with bingo of course – a way to a man's heart and all that. Well, maybe not the bingo.

He hasn't got that effect on me. I'm not swayed. Oh, he's tried, believe me, he's tried.

'Haven't we met before?' He runs a manicured hand through thick silver hair and smiles in a familiar way that might make another's heart a-flutter. 'I'm sure I'd have remembered those eyes.'

He looks intrigued, as if he thinks that he and I.... But eye colour is easy to change these days and I'm not one to be sidetracked. I don't answer him.

'Cat got your tongue, young lady? Don't tell me you're shy, eh?' His arm creeps around my waist.

I step back. 'No. You don't know me.' I manage to say it without spitting. Years of good food, hair dye and brown contacts make a difference that's not easily detected.

'Your name....?'

'Is Bella. And you really don't know me Mr...?'

'Call me Sam... Sammy Barnett. You remind me of a girlfriend I once had. Isa Turnbull she was called. What a looker she was. But that was years ago, before I got this urge to settle down. What say you and me settle down together? Bella....beautiful Bella.'

Oh he hasn't lost the knack. I've heard those words before. He doesn't fool me. 'If you'll excuse me, Mr Barnett,' I say. 'I have things to do – to prepare for tomorrow – for the broth and stotty night.'

'Call me Sammy, Bella, I insist. And I'll let you into a secret.' He bends his head and his lips deliberately brush my cheek as he whispers in my ear. 'I don't like broth, and I prefer my stotty cake with a good bit of meat in it, something to get my teeth into, not to dip into some glorified soup.'

Don't I already know that? 'Well, let's hope you get what you like, Mr Barnett.' Or what you deserve, I add under my breath. I'll certainly give you something you can get your teeth into. I brush my cheek with my hand, as if swatting away an irritating fly.

Back home I take the ox tongue (bought from Bolam's at Sedgefield yesterday) out of the fridge. It's a good buy because it's already pickled using Rick Stein's recipe so I'm saved days of preparation. I cut off the sealed plastic covering and beads of blood-red brine drop off the glistening tongue like rubies as I lower it into the boiling stock of carrot, onion and celery. Ruby – the colour of passion, of heat of the moment, of red hot words spoken with a false tongue! He promised me rubies; he promised me the world. I add six peppercorns, two bay leaves and a glass of good red wine. Wine loosens the tongue. It makes it say things it shouldn't. It makes it try French kissing. It makes a young girl do more things she shouldn't, which makes other tongues set to wagging. I slam the lid on the pot and simmer for five hours.

When it's cooked I plunge the kitchen knife into the beast's tongue, cutting through from root to tip, exposing the dark flesh that hides lies, half-lies and make-believe. Carefully I remove the skin. It's hot and peels away like a rubber mask. Then I curl each half, yin-yang style, into a deep dish. I take a pint of the hot stock and dissolve in it a single ounce of gelatine, stirring all the time until the granules are gone. Then I add another ingredient, not in the recipe: one that I grind up small and stir in until the grains disappear in the hot liquid. And I pour this over the tongue until it is covered. I place a plate on top and weigh it down with tins, not unlike those that weren't tied on the wedding car I never had.

When it's cool, it goes in the fridge overnight. It needs to be chilled. After all, they do say revenge is a dish best served cold.

The next morning the pressed tongue turns out perfectly. A half globe of good red meat and savoury jelly that I cut generously and serve in a stotty cake cut into quarters and decorate with vine tomatoes. A way to a certain man's heart indeed.

I wrap the rest of the meat in four thicknesses of tin foil. It will go into the incinerator at the centre later. One can't be too careful.

That evening, with the smell of set-on vegetables thick in the air, the other ladies are none too pleased when Sammy Barnett bypasses the broth and heads straight for the butties. He leaves none for anyone else. He always was a greedy man, taking it all, when it's something he wants. I was counting on that. He never did have consideration for consequences.

This time it's just as well.

The Paramedics say it's a stroke. Ah *stroke*! Such a word, soft, silky and sensuous. Not really the right word for something that's more like a slap, a blow or even the knockout hit of sleeping pills. Sam Barnett looks groggy. He points at me and tries to speak, but his tongue can't form the words. Then I see a glimmer of knowing in his eyes instead when I poke my tongue out at him, holding its tip between two rows of what are now sadly false but still perfect teeth. I can't help it.

That's something I used to do back then when we were sweethearts, when I was still happy to tease. Who's tongue-tied now, Sammy? I say to myself as they carry him out.

*This story came from a visit to a local community centre where everyone there was female – and I got to thinking what if a man appeared! Also it comments on how everyone makes broth (a North-East favourite) a different way and the old adage about too many cooks spoiling the broth holds here. The recipe for pressed tongue is one I do for special occasions – although people will be pleased to hear I don't add the wine or the sleeping pills.*

# The Dead Woods

Terry Dobson

It slumbers now its dark heart nestling
in the Dead Woods north of Horden Hall,
as it has for untold centuries
a forgotten god in an ancient place.
Unseen tendrils stretch in all directions,
a monumental spider's web
neither bird nor animal abides there
the sullen trees a silent grove
dark and chilling beneath their roots
lies evil incarnate in essence and presence
yet even as it sleeps it feeds on black emotions
a leech on anger, despair, depression
a psychic vampire preying upon the hopeless.
In raptures, the rage of striking miners
and the aftermath of unemployment
and community destruction called it forth
to feast its tentacles spread beneath our feet
occasionally it awakens
and upon waking calls out for sacrifice
with rope or gun or knife
needing to devour the life
of someone in torment
the cries of the suicidal soul
it gorges itself at the cemetery to the west
on grief and tears,
and yet it shies away from playgrounds
places full of laughter and hope,
anathema to its desires.
It withdraws in agony from love
and joy, music and dance,
from happy times of awe and wonder.
So arm yourselves with smiles
reach out a friendly hand
and create here and now a beacon
of light for the world.

# The Writer - Tale of a Verbal Vampire

## Ann Peel

I stand here from nine to five, changing heads at regular intervals. Just a trim, a change of style, get rid of curls, on occasion add a few. There is one constant, I listen.

Some speak quite freely, others need the odd prompt. Then there are the more interesting ones, who make me feel more like a dentist than a barber. It really is a difficult task getting information from them. Their dour personalities, made so by long, lonely shifts in deep, dark places. These miners are a special breed, very often I discover the most refined and subtle thoughts are hidden behind a mask of coarse features and work-scarred skin.

Looking past the basic human thoughts I find some of the freest minds and such deep intelligence that makes me wonder why they took up the work in the first place. Sometimes I sense that no choice was offered, coal was tradition, follow in father's footsteps, earning money now being more important than completing education and taking that step to something a little higher. A bit like myself really. My father was a barber, so I became a barber, but I will not allow my Sonia to touch hair, no way, her brain is too sharp. Her mind-set is academic, two more years at Oxford and she can choose to be whatever she chooses to be.

I know each head, each scalp's detail and sometimes it is a relief to see a new face, listen to what a new mind has to reveal to me. When I get home at night I preserve on paper the thoughts of that day. I have not yet discovered a new Chairman Mao, but I do appreciate the profundity of the thoughts of miner Bill, hearing the smattering of local news from tobacconist Jake. Adding them together gives me a character of dark intelligence and light humour. Neither man will recognise himself because they become a conglomerate. None of my characters are based on any single person, that is what will make good reading, the fact that each reader will see a little of themselves when they read the published copy.

Horden has grown up while I have worked, and so have I. My work too has changed. In the old days we had to serve men and women, boys and girls.

I smile at the thought of all those girls with the female equivalent of a short back and sides. A fringe cut just above the eyebrows and hair cut straight across the back from earlobe to earlobe, neck shaved to look tidy. Now as adults those women must hate my father and myself for the unwelcome gift of hair that, now strengthened and left to grow, meets and sometimes even dips below the collar line.

Even they had thoughts for me and how I enjoyed pouring into my own mind those bright, sparkling, kingfisher thoughts and I am truly happy that I began to collect them in my word purses. Book after book, treasured thoughts, added to daily, so that over the years they join together into a wonderful landscape of Horden, a collection of sounds, smells, sights and memories that will reflect this village that has forged, melded, charged and redesigned so many lives, including mine. This is the reason that I have determined that my Sonia *will* escape.

This hollow life is not for her; she will not follow such mundane strictures. I have helped her to live above the commonplace. She will stay free of the enslavement to the traditions of this place. Sonia will use parfum not scent. She will eat brioche, not stottie cake. My daughter will drink Evian not tap water and she will be dressed by Dior, not Woolworth. My life is as it is so that she can benefit.

What do they think of me, these victims of my mind leeching? Do they even suspect that I feed on their thoughts and feelings? Why should I care, I do not hurt them, their thoughts are given freely and they are not aware that they are keeping my daughter away from the pain of accepting a life of drudgery or mind-numbing servitude that poverty imposes on the majority of the population of this colliery village. They have my eternal gratitude, because of them Sonia will be free to follow her own life course and I, well, when I retire from using the tools of this trade, those word purses contain enough information to continue my true trade-at-hand. The name I write under is unrecognisable, my biography omits any clues to the truth. My books are not my own, they reflect the thoughts of a whole pit village. The whole community supplied the means of educating my girl, ensuring she wanted for nothing that would assist her in life. Not even Sonia, or Dorothy, my long-suffering wife, know that I am a famous author.

It is a shame that I will not be there when they find out. My whole pleasure is my anonymity. What good is a secret shared? Like all vampires, I am excited by the fact that the pleasure is not in the taking but in the keeping and using without discovery. No discovery, no attack: no attack, continued pleasure, contentment.

We are all happy, the village with its listening post, my wife with her home and relative comfort, myself with my secret and best of all my daughter will reach her full potential and maybe, her ambition, whatever it may be, possibly to carry on the *true* family trade..... at a higher level of course.

# The Slasher

## Agnes Frain

All was peaceful in the Logan family's allotment.

Early spring had arrived and the birds were busy; they pecked around the loosened soil desperate for worms to feed their fledglings. The area was ripe with the smell of fertiliser and manure. Spades clinked as they sliced into soil; the chatter of busy men buzzed from garden to garden. Soon their patch of land would be fruitful. The allotment gate clicked as Molly's dad pushed it open. Jack and Daniel rushed to hug their granddad. He swept off his cap to reveal two lollipops.

Adrian quietly groaned. This was his father-in-law Alec's first visit to the garden since he'd viewed the rubble-filled area that had previously passed as an allotment.

Molly hugged her dad, 'We didn't expect you today dad. You must be tired. Is mum busy with the unpacking?'

'You know your mother. She couldn't wait to get the washer on. She chased me out. Home a few hours and already back in her routine. She wants you to call in. There's some presents for the boys. I told her they get far too much but your mum never listens to me. We spent half our holidays trawling around shops.' Alec grimaced in disgust, his deeply lined face drooped.

Molly guessed he'd found plenty to frown about. She raised her eyebrows, 'Go on dad, I bet mum dashed around the last day, three months of sunshine and you still grumble.'

Molly watched Adrian step forward to shake her dad's hand and enquire about their holidays.

Her husband's muscular back tensed and Molly studied the neatness of his ears, partly covered by his thick auburn hair, a line of sweat ran down the back of his blue shirt. Molly fretted. Adrian's bright green eyes were usually full of laughter. But as soon as her father started his jibes, her husband closed up, his face became tight and his leg began to twitch.

Alec swivelled his neck in a stiff rheumatic gesture. He surveyed the newly planted allotment, and then began to prowl. He questioned the need for all the different sized raised beds. Molly slunk away to the safety of the greenhouse when the two combatants limbered up. Would this nonsense ever stop? Why did there always have to be fractious undercurrents every time these two men met?

Adrian was a good man. Hadn't he proved that by settling in her home village and not in his Yorkshire home town? For years they'd squashed into tiny flats. When his hard work had been rewarded and he'd gained his position as a horticulturist for Durham County Council she was delighted. She loved the view of the sea and the distant horizon instead of being swallowed by tall grey buildings.

The boys continued their game as her dad shuffled around the garden. She watched Jack pull his granddad towards an empty bed. Jack held one hand high; she guessed he was trying to explain the height of the sunflowers when they bloomed. Molly pushed open the greenhouse door to catch his remarks. Alec turned to Adrian, 'So, this is what fancy education is all about? To make a garden look like a patchwork quilt.' His tone was indignant.

Molly bit her lip. Her dad was a rude beggar. *Now* what was he doing?

The tyrant's hands were deep in the empty bed; he rubbed his hands through the finely raked soil. 'Adrian!' he shouted across the garden to the younger man who raised his head from his task. Adrian's eyes darkened. His wife flinched. She knew he was mentally donning his armour ready for the tyrant's sharp arrows.

'Look! This is a good spot for leeks, grow some leeks,' Alec smirked. 'Better still grow some for the Show. It needs new life.' He winked. 'You might even beat me.' He slapped his thigh, pleased with his own wit.

Molly strolled out of her refuge, in time to hear the quiet reply.

'That bed is the boy's special place. They want to grow some flowers, and our Jack's keen to grow some courgettes and peppers. We've plenty of room for our needs, I've promised the boys they can plant whatever they fancy there.'

Alec looked at Molly, his face showed disapproval.

'It's our garden, dad, our choice, not yours,' she said.

'That foreign muck! What next - peppers, chillies? ' He waved his hand around the garden. 'All this space took up with fiddly beds. Look at the paths. What a waste of time and space.'

F. Naughton

Adrian gave one of his killer grins, his mouth was smiling but his eyes were pure steel. 'We've ordered this polytunnel to go behind the greenhouse.' He looked at his wife then faced his tormenter. 'I'll grow some leeks in there and some more foreign muck. But only if the loser gives a hundred pound to Cancer Research.' He waited, his stance relaxed, but Molly noticed his leg twitched.

She placed her hand in his and gave a gentle squeeze.

Alec floundered. He wasn't a generous man in any aspect of his character and a hard upbringing, buried in the middle of a large family, had taught him to grow a tough shell. Molly's lively mother was the only one he allowed to penetrate his steel wall.

'Dad.' Daniel swung on Adrian's arm. 'Dad, granddad says you're not a proper gardener because you go to work in a suit.' He continued his swinging. 'But you are, aren't you dad, a proper gardener? '

With a sheepish expression, Alec looked away, then retorted, 'I only said experience beats education hands down and that's a fact.

Adrian's face was grim. The silence between the two men stretched. Molly ushered her sons into the potting shed. She noted her dad's face was red.

Alec flapped his hands. 'OK! If I lose, then charity gets a hundred pounds, will that satisfy you?' Without waiting for a reply, he continued, 'You'll have to join the Leek Club and pay your subscription, like. You can't just waltz in and slap down some leeks.'

Education complete, he nodded sagely to his son-in-law, pulled his cap firmly onto his head, clasped his hands behind his back and walked out of the gate without a backward glance.

The soil was warm, weeks of mild weather had encouraged the plants to emerge and thrust their heads high to bask in the sunlight. The pristine white of the cauliflowers complimented the green of other vegetables. Jack's sunflowers stretched tall, their large round yellow heads swayed in a soft breeze.

One day Molly was sitting on a bench opposite the polytunnel enjoying the fresh flavour of a recently picked tomato. The smell of the vines washed over her senses. She slurped when juice ran down her chin. With a guilty swipe she rubbed at the excess juice. What would her class of young children think if they saw the teacher who insisted they ate their dinners in a neat and tidy way dribbling?

Her husband was pouring a glutinous mixture of feed into bottles stuck upside down near each leek. What was in this mixture remained a mystery to Molly; the rich smell mixed with the odour of compost was nectar so Adrian believed. The leeks thrived; their skin gleamed white and unblemished. The Show was imminent; Adrian's membership number and the name of the club were stamped on the leeks he'd chosen to enter.

Molly wished it was over, and then maybe her dad would stop this nonsense. He was forever spying through the allotment fence on his way to his own patch of land; his hovering cap was easy to spot.

Adrian fought to keep the dialogue going but there was still unease during family visits. Her dad relished in snide remarks and scathing comments. When would her dad accept the difference between him and Adrian?

Blackness. The sky was heavy with clouds that blocked out the moonlight; pinpricks of light glowed from distant street lamps but failed to penetrate the dirt track between the allotments.

A man skulked, head down, face blackened. He blended into the darkness. Wood creaked as the fences breathed; he stopped, his ears pricked like scavenging vermin. He stood motionless and then pulled down his balaclava, now only the whites of his eyes showed.

Something ran over his feet, he gave a little screech of terror and kicked out wildly. His foot caught a soft object that flew in the air. He shuddered as it squealed in rage; he tucked his trousers into his socks and increased his pace. He shone a small torch to get his bearing then quickly climbed over a tall fence and dropped like a cat, then crouched as he surveyed the allotment.

Voices! He scrambled on his knees towards the greenhouse and flattened himself behind a water barrel. All he could see were vague shapes, it was quiet again except for the rustle of grass as night creatures prowled.

Night scented stock perfumed the air. The voices grew louder, he held his breath till they faded, confident now he realised it was only home goers trailing up cemetery bank.

The polytunnel beckoned, he wriggled inside and pointed the torch to the floor and a sliver of light identified the leeks. Untroubled by scruples, he slashed, his knife sharpened to a point whipped through the air, not one leek escaped the violence.

Heavy rain clouds gathered and dropped their burden and a sharp wind sliced through the village. The Show day had arrived.

The allotments were full of helpers clad in rain-wear and Wellingtons. They'd come to admire and praise. Leeks were gently eased from the earth before being borne away to be groomed, washed and pampered.

A tense crowd began to accumulate in Adrian's garden. Some men packed inside the polytunnel while others hovered outside. Angry murmurs drifted, shocked at the devastation, then, as one, the men were silent. Alec pushed and elbowed his way through the crowd, his colour drained and his lined face sagged when he reached the front and gazed at the gaping, ruined leeks.

Molly was shocked, her dad looked very vulnerable. He grasped Adrian's arm and cursed loudly and bitterly at the cruelty. Molly watched as Adrian patted his father-in-law on his bowed shoulders. Still nobody spoke. The air sizzled with tension. The crowd stood, unmoving.

Alec seemed to shrink, his eyes found his daughter's; he hung his head and dropped his hand from his son-in-law's arm.

'I know what you're all thinking, well you're wrong. I wouldn't do this to anybody, never mind one of mine.' He lifted his head and glared at the jury, 'I know I'm an awkward beggar and rude, but that's me. I don't really mean it. Has anybody here ever seen me go out of my way to cause trouble? My mouth has a life of its own but disloyalty and sheer bloody wickedness is not for me.'

Molly held her dad's trembling hand as he continued, 'Well, one thing for sure, I won't be showing my leeks. Whoever did this must be pretty desperate. He's to be pitied. If I never win another show I'll not fret, not after this nastiness.'

The rain had passed, but swirling winds rattled the potting shed windows where the family huddled. Hot tea steamed from thick mugs.

Molly was bewildered by the events of this never-to-be-forgotten day. Plants danced madly as they clung to the soil, but the storm was over. Alec's and Adrian's heads were close. They were discussing the option of seeds for the next Show.

*Before the closure of the collieries the miners had many hobbies. Prize leek growing was high on their list. Prize money was high, members paid a weekly fee plus the breweries gave each club a substantial gift towards the prizes. They did this not out of generosity but because they expected their profits to soar on Leek Show weekends. The clubs were packed and people came from neighbouring villages to view the monsters as they lay gleaming on trestles. There was great skill in producing the best leeks. How they were fed varied from man to man. The rivalry was intense, winners were admired and brains picked for the secret ingredients. Leek slashing was a sad fact but was uncommon.*

# Eating Jelly in the Welly

## Chris Robinson

I'm eating jelly in the Welly
With me Ma and me Da
Uncle Ted, Auntie Sue
Cousin Jack, Gran and Grandpa too

We came to enjoy
The hot summer sun
To have a relax
And some family fun

We took sandwiches
Pies, jelly and pop
And bought saveloys
From the butcher's shop

We took bats and balls

Eating jelly in the Welly
Other games to play
Lots to amuse us
Throughout the whole day

Gran had her knitting
Auntie Sue did too
Uncle Ted and Da
Discussed their home brew

I'm eating jelly in the Welly
With me Ma and me Da
Uncle Ted, Auntie Sue
Cousin Jack, Gran and Grandpa too.

# Things Are Different Now

## David Lee

A year ago on a cloudy but warm day in June, I was sitting at my desk doing the online shopping for the week. I noticed a few teenagers hanging around, in the back garden, looking rather fed up with themselves. I waved at them and they acknowledged me.

Then I thought about this. What are they doing just hanging around?

I would like to know what is going on in their minds. Maybe they are fearful of what the future may hold for them. No one knows this. After all I was young person once in my life.

Just then a knock came to the door. My nephew Tony walked in, as he does, to see me. He is 18 years of age, likes a pint now and then. Has spiky hair stuck up with gel. Tony loves music, enjoys the computer, loves DVDs. Power Ranger's his favourite ones. He goes to a live show with his Uncle Ben. Tony has a girlfriend also - above all - he is a caring person.

'Not another one! What's up with you? You look as if you found a shilling and lost a fiver! Everyone seems browned off with everything. It is a beautiful day outside. Not much sun but still warm'.

'It's just that there's nothing to do. We cannot express ourselves the way I'd like to do. When all of us are in a group, the police move us on. All through mindless idiots. But my friends never do harm to no one.'

'Are you drinking outside Tony? '

'No Uncle Ben, we are not.'

'Well, because older people see a group like yours and they panic and call for help.'

Then Tony asked me, 'What was it like in your days Uncle Ben?'

'When I was your age, Tony, I was on a building site at Rosebyrd in Horden, knocking down prefabs ready to build new houses. We worked there for 2 years or more. It was hard work.' I paused, remembering. 'In 1966 the winters were hard. They seemed to last for ever Tony. We used to clean paths for the old folks. There was a job for me at S.C.A Hartlepool. 21 years I worked there. I loved to play darts for the Friday darts and Wednesday Leagues. I was heavily involved with the church of St Mary's Horden. I served for 38 years. A happy marriage to Carol. Good job I did things when I could.'

I continued, 'A word of advice,Tony! Grab what you can in your life. Don't wait. Today we saw what you could be doing Tony, and you rejected it. I hate to see that happening now.'

I went on. 'In my time there was no drinking outside. Just beer gardens. I was 21 then. Never drank until my 21st birthday with a few of my friends. We drank sensibly. That's how it was then.'

Tony said, 'Uncle Ben they try to pass drugs on to us.'

'Have you taken any drugs, Tony?'

'No I haven't, Uncle Ben.'

'Look! Life's not a bed of roses. We are all in the School of Hard Knocks.'

'What will you do when you leave school Tony?'

'I think I'll do computers, Uncle Ben.'

Outside there was the sound of a bottle being smashed. Breaking glass. Oh no! Not again.

'Call for help, Tony.'

Things are different now, aren't they?

# The Beach

## Ann Peel

They've pulled my teeth removed my braces
Taken away external traces
My face is clean, a pristine land
Can't quite disguise coal peppered sand
Remember days when dross would spew
And cover jewels of brilliant hue
Now ochre, grey and off white sands
Hide coal truck's deeply driven bands.
Fishermen there, children play too,
Listening to cries of gull and curlew
No longer hear the falling shale
No longer see a grounded whale.
You cleaned me up, or so you say
What of the life you took away
No *Good News Week* to bring to life
A working beach well used to strife.
I may be cleaner, but I'm sad
No longer see the working lad
When you go home and leave me here
The sea can't wash away my tear
The tear I shed for life gone by
For kites the kids flew in my sky
For fires beside a fishing pole
The miners' kids gave me my soul.

*A lot of money has been spent on removing all traces of mining activity on the North East Coast.
But for me, even the encouragement of the re-growth of original flora does not replace the lost character
of the sanitised beaches of Horden and Easington.*

# Mouse City

## Agnes Frain

Our street is filled with noise: the chants of skippers and the slap of rope, the yells of cowboys, the bangs of cap guns and the laughter of children.

Irate housewives fight for space to stretch their drying lines: they flap away nosey kids. Even on this warm day, smoke belches from blackened chimneys. Fires are still ablaze in the huge black-leaded ranges, home to ovens and set-pots full of hot water. Cooking smells waft from kitchen doors mixed with the scent of soap powder.

It's Monday: the day when all respectable women toil over wash tubs. There is a rush to be the first to hang out snow-white laundry on their lines.

This is our first day of freedom, everything is fresh, a wonderful novelty. Miss a minute of our holiday, not likely! Future days of rain and boredom, unthinkable. This is today; tomorrow can look after itself.

Two hands cupped, I bounce the balls against the wooden hatch set in the coal house wall. Manipulating two balls together is a new skill and it takes all my concentration. One blink and the rhythm will be ruined.

'BANG!' A cap explodes near my ear. The balls scatter; my brother runs down the street away from my fury. The balls roll after him till one of them disappears through an open yard gate.

Too late to halt its momentum I hesitate; this was the yard of newcomers. I've watched the family from a distance but they seem to prefer their own company. I glance into the yard. It's a mess and an old shed without a door is packed with worn carpets, newspapers and broken furniture. Dirty curtains hang from unwashed windows. The house looks unloved and neglected.

'Come on, come and get your ball.' A young man raises his head from a fire in a metal dust bin and beckons me forward. My ball is behind a group of smaller kids who are gathered around an old chair. They're untidy with ill-fitting clothes and tangled hair. They are busy with sharp elbows as they fight each other to get to the front of the group.

Curious, I stand on tiptoes to see what the attraction is. I stared in disbelief. Balanced on the chair is a square wooden box, the front is covered with two glass doors. Inside the box are shelves stacked high: multiple shelves, with tiny ladders giving access to each layer.

Mice scramble and scamper. They leap up the ladders, dozens of the tiny creatures. They stream onto the shelves where sparse damp straw is scattered. This is a high-rise mouse city. They are like clowns. They flip over in somersaults off the shelves and sheer numbers push some of them over the edges. Small mice are huddled together for protection, flattened into corners. Their whiskers quiver and wet pink tongues flick from their tiny mouths.

Unable to avert my eyes I view these prisoners as they fight for survival; individuals are using their teeth to scratch and bite as they hunt for a space in the melée. A mouse shaped damp straw into a nest and wriggled inside, other mice were licking the doors, mouths open, mute.

I shake with revulsion at the sight of so many helpless creatures piled on top of each other. Covering my mouth, I fight against the contents of my stomach as I retch. My legs tremble and I am rooted to the spot.

One of the boys runs to the shed and returns with a plastic spade. The children press closer. He opens a hatch at the side of the box and pushes in his spade. A sweet but pungent smell escaped as with a flourish the wild-eyed boy scooped out a packed heap of straw.

The torturers run with whoops and screeches towards the bin and then throw the contents of the spade into the fire. Tiny, pink hairless mice move feebly in their nest. Still I am rooted, unable to turn away from this nightmarish scene.

Now the young man in charge is red with rage; he grabs a couple of the young kids and hustles them into the house. The spell is broken. I scream at the remainder of the group who giggle, their cruel mouths wide. Now they climb onto the yard wall and then gather like a flock of crows on the coalhouse roof.

I make a tearful escape.

# The Chalk Mark

## Mary N. Bell

Feigning sleep, thirty year old Clive Johnson, secretary of the local miners' lodge, secretary of the local Labour Party, a governor of local schools, with a seat on every committee of Westford Rural District Council, sat in his plush easy chair. His arms rested on the well polished leather. He contemplated the path his life was taking.

A smug smile played at the edges of his lips as he thought of his success before his Saturday night out on the town. A leading member of this thriving community in the Thirties, he'd been a miner with free coal and free house. However he'd rarely worked down the pit because of his position.

The coal owners had recognised Clive as above average in intelligence and willing to arbitrate in disputes. His theory was - work at any price. However low paid you were, working was better than no pay and this suited the owners down to the ground or rather under the ground.

Some spoke disparagingly of Clive, calling him a boss's man. This did not bother him. People also called him a ladies' man. In his late twenties when he married he decided it would be good for his image as a pillar of the community to settle down to a respectable married life. He'd also noted the warning from an elder of the council, and a stalwart of the union, that his fast licentious ways were not going unnoticed and would not be tolerated.

It was always the married ladies who attracted him. He could have had his choice of the single ones. Clandestine affairs with married women were secrets safely kept, because the women didn't wish to be caught and suffer the wrath of irate husbands. Discretion was the first rule for such married women.

Clive married Isabel because she belonged to a respected family. An only child of Matthew and Elsie Sterling, an intelligent girl, she had worked in the local Co-operative Society office and was a Sunday school teacher to boot. For all it was so easy to date and court his willing victim he still enjoyed courting her. His marriage to Isabel solidified his position, his previous exploits being excused as 'sowing of wild oats'.

He met Isabel at a chapel social evening. He noticed her - slim, five foot six inches tall with a peaches and cream complexion. He knew who she was, but he never thought of her in a romantic way till now. Her general appearance was a bit prim but was not bad looking at all. Just right for a wife, he thought. He wondered why she'd reached twenty five without being married.  Still, he courted her. They got engaged. Their big, grand wedding befitted that of the only child of Mr. and Mrs. Sterling.

The first few months of married life were satisfactory. She was not responsive in bed, but she would learn, he thought. When Isabel became pregnant he was the happiest of men. When, in the middle of the pregnancy, she turned away from him because, she said, there was a risk to the baby, he complied with her request and he thought nostalgically of past romances.

After the birth of Flora, an adorable child, Isabel said she could not be with him until she 'felt right' again. Married relations had to be abandoned. By the time Flora was eight years old Isabel still did not 'feel right.'

He buried himself in communal and union work. Isabel was equally busy with chapel work. She was a member of all the chapel groups. She prided herself on her clean house. Clive never had to wait for a meal. She thought she was the perfect wife. Her washing was the cleanest that fluttered on any clothes line.

Then after a time he became aware of a very attractive relief barmaid called Eva Mitchell who lived in Hawthorn Avenue and whose husband George was a hewer at the pit. She had a bubbliness about her that sent sparks of longing throbbing through Clive. He discovered that she did not enjoy living in the narrow streets of closely situated colliery houses with their twitching net curtains.

Clive started to talk to Eva of his married life. He began to call on her. He was surprised at how easy it was to deceive Isabel and George. Hawthorn Avenue was made up of six houses. High walls, hid each back yard from outsiders, and high fences inside hid the houses from prying eyes – all these seemed specially built for Eva and Clive.

Clive would visit Eva during the day when George was at work. He could slip up the back street without being seen. If George was at work Eva would put a chalk mark on the back gate to indicate the coast was clear. Clive had no need to make an excuse to Isabel to his whereabouts - she would think he was at work.

One day, no chalk mark! Then another day no chalk mark! And again. Clive had to stop calling and had no way of contacting Eva.

In time, Eva went back to work at the club. When he challenged her, she said, 'Well, I waited for you all those afternoons! When I went to rub off the white chalk before George got home it was already gone.' She pushed his pint across the counter. 'I thought you'd rubbed it off to let me know you'd passed by.'

The next day Clive concealed himself among the hawthorn bushes and after Eva chalk-marked the gate he saw the neighbour erase it. Spoilsport!

After that Clive would go to the pit time office and check that George's token was missing so he knew that Eva's husband was safely out of the way and he could pay his afternoon visit in safety.

His relationship with Eva progressed and they decided it would be good to go out together. Clive had a cousin, Harry Roberts, a pub landlord in neighbouring Greencroft. He told Isabel he was going to help Harry at the Blue Dog pub on a Saturday night. Eva had always been in the habit of visiting friends at a weekend so it was no problem for her.

A perfect set-up.

Clive even had an alibi for smelling of drink. Isabel had never visited the Blue Dog at Greencroft and had only met Harry when he attended their wedding nine years before.

One night they even went out on a visit to a pub in town. They held hands like the lovers they were. Laughing and flirting, Eva bewitched Clive. Coming home they travelled together as far as a nearby village, where Clive got off the bus and walked the mile home so they were never seen together. Also it helped him to sober up a bit. So this is how the affair progressed. The relationship suited both of them. They enjoyed each others' company and their outside meetings added to the excitement.

One summer evening Clive entered his back street, smugly thinking life was good. 'God's in his heaven, all's right with the world.' Everything was all right in his own world. No chance of ever being found out. He felt ten feet tall, as though he could cart-wheel up the street. But he settled for a satisfied chuckle and he sniggered at the chaste lives of his neighbours.

Some of the them were at their gates, chatting and passing the time of day with any passersby, as was the summertime evening custom. There were more people about than usual. He sensed a buzz of excitement in the air. No one stopped him. They just nodded and watched him. Suddenly he felt apprehensive.

He could see his own house. Was that a policeman emerging from his back gate? He quickened his step. Why had that policeman been to his house? An accident? On a Saturday night? He broke into a run. He flung the door open. Breathless he stood silhouetted in the dusk light, ashen-faced. Isabel was sitting looking shocked.

What had the policeman been to tell her?

She inquired quietly, 'So, have you had a busy night?'

'Yes, the pub was full.'

'Well. The police have been looking for you.' She stared at him. 'Harry Roberts wants you to go and help him.' She looked at him with cold, questioning eyes -'The Blue Dog burned down this afternoon.'

*This comes from two tales. The first was told me many years ago by a miner, and was about a well respected man who had an affair. More recently a woman I know told me how her mother had erased the chalk mark to end an affair.*

# The Durham Rapper

## Susan Robinson

'You know what, love, that lad wasn't the first dancer to come out of Easington.'

I turn to this old bloke with a skinny pony-tail who's sitting behind me. We're up at the school after they've been showing the film *Billy Elliot* to the people of Easington.

'Really?' says I.

I'm about to remind this man that *Billy Elliot's* just a story when he interrupts. 'You'll not know, and you'll not likely believe me either,' he says. 'But miners dance. They do a kind of Morris dancing of their own.'

'You're having me on! No way.'

'Aye,' he says. 'It's right, and I'll tell you how I know. It's like this. Just before the Strike, me and Trev – we were best marras at the pit you know - was picked to carry the banner for Easington at the Big Meeting. We nearly never went though, 'cos Trev's dad was doing his head in. Trev's mam had gone and died, and his dad had got this depression thing. He kept disappearing, like, and wouldn't tell Trev where he'd been. Mainly he'd lock himself in his shed for hours on end, making this hell of a racket. Anyway, I said that if that's the case his dad wouldn't know whether Trev stayed or went. So we went. Do you go to the Big Meeting? No? You'll not know what it's like then.'

The old bloke leans forward in his seat and tells me his story. 'Well, on the way home some of the bands stop to play outside the Dun Cow. It's tradition to stop here, like. It's the oldest pub in Durham. You play outside the County on the way into the Big Meeting, for the crowd and the Big Knobs - the Politicians, NUM officials, and the likes of them; and you play the Dun Cow on the way out.'

'By then like, folks've usually had a few beers too many. The place's always crowded. Everyone hangs around outside taking up most of the road - ready for the bands. All this attracts these mad characters. Rocky always shows up here, strutting and singing his Elvis stuff. The crowd love the whole thing. They'll form this circle, six or more deep. It's a bit of a bear-pit but good natured, if you know what I mean.

'Well, my mate Trev's in a belligerent mood, he usually is after a bevy. Me, it just gives me confidence to tap up the lasses. But him.... he gets really bolshie.

He says, "I'm bloody sick of hanging around man, it's too effing hot. I wouldn't mind if I was carrying the banner pole, but I mean, what do I look like, carrying this bloody rope? Proper Nancy eh! Nobody better laugh at us."

Well, in front of us there's this kiltie band playing the pipes.

Trev chunters on. "Just look at them jessies, man. You wouldn't see *me* dead in a skirt. Do you think its right what they say about them wearing nowt underneath? And I wish they'd play something different to Amazing effing Grace on them pig's bladders. God, I'm knackered, carrying this rope."

Anyway it's what's in front of the pipers that holds everyone up. I reach forward and jostle one of the bear-skinned Scotsmen. I say, "What's the problem mate?"

He shrugs and in turn asks the man in front, who does the same right down the line of pipers. The answer comes back like Chinese whispers. "It's a wee Morris Dance group, man. They've got the place taken."

Well, Trev goes red in the face. "Bloody Hell! Effing Morris Dancers? What's a bunch of prats dressed like poofs prancing around at the Big Meeting for?" He grabs one of the kids who follow the band and gives him the rope. "Keep hold of that, bonny lad. I need a slash and some liquid refreshment. I'll not be long." And he pushes his way through the crowd to the pub, with me after him, just to make sure he comes back, like.

The amber nectar cools our shrivelled throats. Then we shove back through the throng of noisy drinkers to see for ourselves what Morris Team dares dance here, at the Durham Miners' Big Meeting.

And there they are! Only they're not dressed in the usual Morris outfits. You know, white shirts and knee length trousers tied with a sash. And they're not carrying fancy sticks with ribbons and bells on. No, these lads are dressed as miners. Traditional gear, mind, not your fashionable orange overalls. Pit socks and boots, hoggers kept up with string, old patched waistcoats and flat caps on their heads. They've got coal-blackened faces as if they'd come straight from a shift at the pit. And they carry picks and shovels that they bang on the ground, then smash one against the other as they move around in a sort of underground safety ritual; nothing like a dance at all, except they're clashing their steel toe-capped boots off the ground throwing sparks into the air.

The crowd goes wild, cat-calling and whistling, clapping and cheering.

"Why, yer bugger," says I. "Seen nowt like that then, have yer?"

Trev groans. "I don't like it man. Men dancing like pansies, they might look like miners, but I bet none of them's been down the pit." He swallows half his pint in one go, his Adam's apple bobbing like it was Halloween.

Well, just then, the main man of the troop brays his shovel off the ground to get the crowd's attention. I can tell he's the boss, 'cos he wears a leather cap with the peak down the back of his neck, and a miner's lamp hangs off his belt like he's the Deputy.

"And now," he shouts, "we perform the Durham Rapper."

The team put down their picks and shovels and pick up sword-like metal strips. They hold them above their heads, one end in each hand. They shout "Aye Tommy."

"A rapper," says the Boss Man Tommy, "is a flexible piece of metal that was used at one time to scrape coal dust off pit ponies' backs. The rapper dance reflects the special bond miners have. The end result, as you will see, represents the solidarity and union between the tribe of men called miners."

To fiddle, melodeon and concertina, the group of pitmen dancers hold their rappers high and twist and turn in a cats-cradle pattern of a dance, up and over each other, inside out and backside first; blurring the eye and deceiving the ale-fuddled brain.

I glance at Trev. He's got a look on his face like someone's pinched his beer. He's obviously puzzled.

Susan Robinson

"What's up. Trev?"

He points a shaking finger to one of the dancers. "Look, man.... Look...."

Just then the man he's pointing to does a double somersault right in front of us, lands squarely on his feet and stands there grinning, teeth white against his coal face. He holds aloft all the rappers, now woven together in a star shape.

That's when Trev grasps hold of us, and shouts in my ear. "Why, that's me bloody da!"

The crowd go ballistic. The noise is crackers, man. Whistling and stamping. You'd think bloody Arthur Scargill'd come among us. The cry goes up

"He-ero-oh.... He-ero-oh...."

Trev's got a smirk on. He punches the air. "It's me dad." He shouts to whoever will listen.

I've never seen Trev look so chuffed. Think he'd won a Bully at the darts. "Not so much the pansy now, Trev!" I say.

"You shut your mouth," he says to me, smiling like. "That's me da you're talking about!"

\*\*\*

The hall where they showed Billy Elliot is nearly empty now. The man behind pats my shoulder. 'There now lass,' he says. 'What a day that was. There's something you can tell folks when they talk about that Billy Elliot and *his* dancing.' And he laughs and winks at me. Then he gets up and goes.

I never get to know his name.

*This story came out of the ether- or so I thought until I began to research Morris Dancing and found a long history associated with miners. I really hadn't known that this was the case. Perhaps I'd seen a dance team at the Big Meeting when I was a child and then forgotten about it, although to my knowledge there hasn't been one dressed as described in my story.*

# Coal Dust In My Veins

Mary N. Bell

Pits, miners, coal
Companions of my life
Proud pitman's daughter,
Loyal collier's wife
Gallower kist pit prop,
Hewer stoneman putter,
Were the very first words
I was heard to utter.

Deputy Grandad
Easington born and bred,
Poems and stories of coal
Stockpiled in my head
In hundreds of years time
when they dig up my remains
Descendants will find I have
Coal dust in my veins.

F. Naughton

# Beach Banks

Terry Dobson

Early morning peaceful
Rabbits graze wary watchful
A blur of stoat or weasel
Too quick to tell.
Sun shines, larks sing
Nests in wild grasses and flowers
Where once stood spoil heaps
Tall dark barren
Now green for miles
The land dips and rises
Nature in control once more
Building a beautiful landscape.
North over the fields and shrubs,
Lies Easington, look there's Beacon Hill
South I see Blackhall Crimdon
Hartlepool and more.
On the edge looking down
The sea calm today is gentle
As it tastes the pebbles
On the beach.

# The Moods of Blue

Agnes Frain

Winds moan and the sky presses down, shoulders bow in defeat
The sky hides its blue then hovers like a shroud dark and oppressive
My limbs are bound and wrapped in its cruel dark days
Until the colours start to expand, grey is predominant in this fair land
I search in vain as winter creeps, slow it dawdles in view to mock and jibe
My spirits at their lowest ebb dampness knocks on my aching bones

Is that a glimpse have you relented did clear blue squeeze in sight
I'm too old to play hide and seek I give up I submit show yourself
I stretch my freed limbs and my mouth smiles wide
Winter blues slink reluctantly away blown apart by the gentle breeze
The Dene spreads out its sumptuous carpet soft and supple underfoot
Bluebells wave when I amble past they too rejoice and feel uplifted

Sunbeams spread their magic glitter they cut like scythes
Split asunder they show no mercy to the last stragglers clad in grey
No more blue days no more misery no more oppressive grey
Light blue bright blue royal blue clash and jangle as they compete
Their beauty flourishes under the kind blue sky
Cataracts removed as the summer progresses, colours reborn

We store these memories deep secure and unopened
Till the malicious winter, fresh from its travels pounces with renewed power.

David Lee

# The Tunnel: A History

## David Lee

In the year 1603 when King James 1st ruled England a ghost of a lady began to haunt a building called Horden Hall. This was a seventeenth century manor house owned by the Conyers family who had fled when Henry the Eighth brought in the Reformation.

This ghost was called Mary Conyers and one day she stumbled upon the man dressed in a monk's habit. He had been hiding in a secret priest's hole at the back of the old manor. It was two feet under one lot of floorboards and three feet above another set of floorboards. The hole stunk of human flesh and foist from the floor.

At the moment Mary found him they both fell through the floors of the manor house. Down they floated, holding each other's hand, and landed with a bump. They sat and looked around. They were in a man-made tunnel. They looked at each other in amazement.

'Where have you come from?' the monk – whose name was Ambrose – asked her.

'I have been haunting around this old place for more than fifty years,' she said. 'Looking for my family.'

'And why would you do that?'

'Well, I was in love once with a man disapproved of by my family. He loved me so much that he asked my father if he could marry me. But my father refused to let him. Every time he came to see me they hid me in a cupboard. They told me I could not marry anyone from outside the family.'

The monk listened to her very carefully.

She went on. 'I could not look at another man. I was so very unhappy that I died of a broken heart because of what they did to me.'

'Oh dear,' said Ambrose. 'And how old were you when this happened to you?'

'I was twenty five years old,' she said. 'And what about you? Who are you?'

'My name is Ambrose,' he said. 'I am a priest who did not want to serve Rome. So I was brought here by your parents. They were good friends of mine, devoted parishioners of St Mary's at Easington.'

It was getting colder there in the tunnel with an eerie light that seemed to come from the walls. It felt damp and chilly and from somewhere came the sound of running water.

'Let's move on,' she said.

They walked on and on, as much as two miles down there.

Ambrose ducked as bats swooped low around his head. 'Can we rest for awhile?' he said.

She stopped and leaned against a wall. He leaned beside her.

Just then some men, rough looking seamen - perhaps even smugglers - came running down the tunnel. Ambrose stepped in front of them. 'Halt!' he said. 'Why are you running?'

They looked scared for a moment, then one of them said, 'We're running from the coastguards. They caught us landing stuff from the pirates and shot and killed us.' His eyes were full of fear.

Ambrose smiled gently. 'Well, gentlemen, you can stop running now.' He held up his hand and made the sign of the cross and blessed them. This put them at their ease at once. They thanked him and went on their ghostly way.

Ambrose and the lady ghost walked on down the tunnel. They turned a corner and finally felt the cool breeze on them and the sound of water lashing on the sandy beach.

Now they could hear the sound of a boy and girl laughing and dogs barking. They emerged from the mouth of the tunnel into the day.

'Look!' said the boy. 'Ghosts!'

'Ghosts!' said the girl.

And they ran away.

Ambrose and the lady took a last look at the sea and disappeared.

# Harry's Bogey

## Susan Robinson

'I'm not taking him, mind.'

'Who?'

'My Granda.'

'Taking him where?'

'To school. Mrs Thom's doing this inter-generation thing.' He reads from a crumpled letter he pulls out of his pocket. 'She's having a *Take Your Granddad To School Day.*'

'Oh! That's lovely pet.'

'I'm not taking him.'

'Why not? He'd like that.'

'Cos he's daft, he pretends. And he'll show me up, like he does.'

'He's not daft, Harry pet. He's got this illness called Alzheimer's. It's just mild though, nothing to worry about.'

The granddads sit on the child-size seats at the square tables in Year Four classroom - nothing like the kind of classroom they remember. They look slightly chuffed with themselves, with their names on labels stuck to the front of their clothes. They smile and chatter non-stop to each other as they share memories of when they'd last been in school. It's all rather noisy. The kids these granddads belong to sit in silence, in rows in the front. They know how to behave while they wait for Mrs Thom to introduce the session.

Sid Herbert, Harry's Granda, polishes his glasses with a corner of his cardigan. He knows why he's here. His daughter Denise, Harry's mam, told him this morning that he was going to school with Harry to tell the children about what school had been like when he was a lad.

'You'll be all right Dad. Just tell them how it was. You remember, don't you? You always had tales to tell me when I was a kid. You know, all the boys separate from the girls in that big old school down the street. The one that's a proper eyesore these days, it should be knocked down. What about the times you got the cane – kids don't know what a cane is today. Anyway, enjoy yourself and I'll see you later.'

Each granddad has a turn. They have to stand up in front of the class and tell a story about their experience at the old Easington Colliery Junior Boys School.

'We wore short trousers and scraped knees, short back and sides haircuts.'

'There were teachers that terrified and those that didn't, like Mr Wilson - a lovely man who looked like Inspector Lockhart off the tele: black and white mind in our day.'

'Milk in glass bottles that tasted horrible when it was warmed on radiator pipes on cold days, so that the frozen milk pushed up the tin-foil tops.'

'Outdoor toilets built of brown enamel bricks that didn't show stains and smelled of pee; and concrete stairs to the upper classrooms.'

'We had proper dinners, mind, mashed potato with everything and pudding with custard - all scoffed so quickly that bellies still felt empty afterwards. Nothing left, even stuff you didn't like – you were made to eat it - especially when you were reminded that children in Africa were starving.'

'Everyone did as they were told, like.'

'When we sang *Onward Christian Soldiers* in the hall – we sounded like a boys' army. We sounded great.'

'Me? When I was a lad I'd disappear at break time to put in a load of coal in and come back and sit in class – black as the roads. The headmaster then had a special bamboo cane with a curved handle; it could really make hands sting. It even had its own name.'

'Can you remember what it was?'

'Nah, but once I was sent for the cane I brought it back to the class in pieces held together with strands from the bamboo. Told him, "I dropped it, sir." "A likely tale," he says.

Now at last it's Sid's turn. He stands up, straightens his glasses and marches out to the front of the class. He stands to attention, feet together, eyes forward. He isn't nervous. He hasn't done anything wrong. He won't be caned this time. He's not stupid. He tries to remember what it is he's going to say. The stories won't come out in a straight line; they're all meshed together in his brain, mixed up with what all the other granddads have already said. Then he has a genius thought.

'I'm going to tell you about the annual Bogey Race between Easington and Horden Boys' Schools.'

'What's a Bogey, mister?'

'It's snot!' shouts one small boy.

'A snot race?'

Everyone laughs except Harry.

'Quiet now, children. Listen to Mr Herbert,' says Mrs Thom.

'A Bogey,' says Sid 'was a cart, like a modern go-cart only home-made. We used to make them out of anything we could get our hands on, planks of wood, pram wheels, vegetable crates, anything. The frame had two crossbars with wheels and a couple of planks nailed on joining the two together with a bit of old carpet for a seat stuck on the back.' Sid's hands wave around in the air as he tries to describe what he means. 'You steered it with your feet on the front crossbar that had a bit of rope through to hold on to. And there weren't any brakes; you just used your feet to stop.'

Sid feels rather hot. He takes off his coat and unbuttons his cardigan. He's forgotten that he's left his pyjamas on underneath because it makes life easier at bedtimes. Harry looks at him strangely. Is his hair sticking up again? Harry's always telling him to brush his hair, what there is of it. He runs an absent hand over his own head.

'Well, anyway, like I said we had a race every year between the schools. The boys' schools that is. Girls didn't make bogeys. One year it was held in Easington, the next in Horden. The Easington race ran from the Waterworks right down Seaside Lane, down Office Street and under the first bridge. The Horden race came down Ellison's Bank, past the top Park and ended as near to the Co-op as possible. Well, the year I won, I'd got such a speed up coming down the bank that I careered past the Co-op, past The North Eastern, down Alder Road, under the railway bridge, down Limekiln Gill and onto the beach like I was the Flying Scotsman. I'm telling yer. Folks couldn't believe it.' Sid blinks and looks around. The kids sit dumbfounded. Harry has his face in his hands. The other granddads wink and nod at each other.

Mrs Thom leads the clapping, everyone joins in; everyone except Harry. 'That was wonderful,' she says. 'May I say thank you to all the granddads, particularly Mr Herbert who has entertained us with such a fascinating tale. After dinner children I think it would be a good idea for you to design and draw your very own bogey. Don't forget they can be made out of anything at all. Be imaginative.'

Harry's drawing is the best, said Mrs Thom later. It's a red Speedo pod with skateboard wheels. The driver has to lie down on his tummy and steer with a TV remote, using the cursor buttons to change direction. It goes as fast as a bullet and is slowed by a kite-like parachute that snakes like a sidewinder.

'Most inventive. You must take after your granddad, Harry. I imagine your family are proud of him, winning that race, and all.'

Harry grins, he can't wait to get home to show his granda the drawing of his bogey.

# Goodtime Gertie

## Joan Wright

St Peter woke up with a start
Twas a rattling at the gate
He said, somebody's early
As he put his halo straight.
As he floated to the gate
It opened inches wide
And he gazed in stunned amazement
At one who stood outside.
Once a bonny colliery lass
Who never would be led
Until a strapping mining lad
Took her behind his shed
Now known as Goodtime Gertie
She gave a toothless grin
I've gone and popped my clogs she said
So haway let me in.
But this is paradise he said
It's not for such as you
You've not been good but very bad
So I can't let you through
What do you mean she said aggrieved
Mankind did not complain
They'd come a knocking on my door
And pleased would come again
The Lord says give mankind your love
So that is what I did
No fella did I turn away
And I only charged ten quid
You got his message wrong, my child
That isn't what he meant
So you are scheduled for below
And that's where you'll be sent
She peered through the pearly gate
And said, it does look glum
Let me in I promise you
I'll soon make it hum
We're angels said St Peter
We cannot let sinners in

She said I bet I've had more fun
Than you have had hot dinners
He sighed and said Oh Gertie
When you went astray
We asked the good lord what to do
And all he said was pray
But in your case it was in vain
You came to be regarded as
A blot on his creation
So down below is where you go
But I'll tell you what I'll do
In case you're feeling nervous
I'll travel down with you
Oh no you won't a voice boomed out
It was the voice of God
Your place is here and here you'll stay
Unless I give the nod
I'll take Gertie down below
It's time for my survey
Errol Flynn gives me the gen
I have him in my pay
Oooh is Errol Flynn below
My idol of the screen
I used to wish he was my rent man
She winked, know what I mean?
I'd dream that I was stony broke
And the rent I couldn't pay
And he say, well in lieu of rent
Let's go and hit the hay
I always thought that heaven
Was the place for me to be
But if Errol Flynn's below
Then that's the place for me
Errol and his naughty ways
My time there will be swell
Wait til I put my teeth back in
Then I'll gladly go to hell!

# Fairground Ride

## Ann Peel

The three girls were excited, walking quickly, arms linked, along Sunderland Road to the spare ground just before the Crossroads. The Shows were here again! Didn't seem like a year since they were last here, did it? They were grown up now and all three felt it.

That was until they saw the Waltzer, their favourite ride, mainly because the boys who worked on it could spin your shell so fast it was difficult to walk straight when you got off. So much fun! Because they were now 16 years old they knew that their shell would be one to concentrate on, for those dark foreign-looking gypsy boys had such an air of mystery, a thing no Horden boy could ever have.

When they arrived the Waltzer was already in motion and Sheila saw the young man - tall, gaunt, dark wavy hair and eyes so dark it was hard to tell where iris began and pupil ended. His hair kept falling over his eyes as he pushed the shell containing some other girls already on his magical machine.

When the ride stopped Sheila, Jane and Maggie clambered into the nearest shell and each of them shivered with anticipation as he came toward them casually reaching out a hand to take their money, clasping fingers before moving on. The music changed and the ride gathered pace. The man came across nonchalantly to spin them and the girls all screamed with pure pleasure.

All too soon the ride was over. The young man ignored Jane and Margaret's efforts to get his attention but firmly held Sheila around the waist until she was safely to earth again.

'Off for a break,' he called to his friends, not letting go of Sheila. She was doubly happy now. He asked her name and she told him. He said his name was Carlos. How romantic, he was Spanish!

They stopped and bought pop from a stall nearby. She asked how long he'd been in the country and listened, enthralled, as he described his exciting and adventurous life. What a wonderful thing to be able to tell her parents about this wonderful, exciting, foreign lad who had entered her life in such a romantic way.

A voice from behind them. 'All right Johnny, time to get back to work, the boss is looking for you.'

Johnny? Lead balloon or what? Sheila ran.

A week later the three girls were together again in Moscardini's, discussing the previous Saturday, when Sheila had almost been taken in by that fairground lothario. The door opened and all eyes turned to it automatically and there he was! The subject of conversation. Walking directly to their table he asked if he could sit down and all three spoke at once saying, 'It's a free world.'

Leaning forward he offered all three a drink but his eyes were on Sheila who looked down and refused to meet his gaze. When he had bought Cokes for the other two and a coffee for himself, Johnny started to explain himself as if he and Sheila were alone. 'I am so sorry that that all happened last week,' he said, 'I just wanted to impress you and realise now, how daft you must think I am.'

All three girls nodded and Sheila looked up into those dark, persuasive eyes. Johnny went on to explain that he'd just left the Navy and the job had been temporary. Now he had a permanent one there was no need to pretend anymore. He could be himself.

Sheila sighed and gave in, Spanish or not, they had a real connection that she could not even hope to deny.

Their friendship continued and her parents, having heard she was 'walking out', started to ask questions. She answered them all openly.

Name? - Johnny, haven't asked the surname yet!

Age? - nearly 22, from - Hetton le Hole.

Job? - just out of the Navy, now a musician.

Mum and dad looked concernedly at each other and asked if she would bring him home to meet them. They were told no. He would think she was trying to corner him!

The next time they met Sheila told Johnny about how strange her parents were acting and of their request to meet him. 'But, of course, you don't need to.'

She felt that he was such a sweetie when he said, 'Well if it stops them worrying I'll come now if you like!'

On entering the front door, Sheila called, 'We're here mum, I brought Johnny to see you!'

Mum came forward frowning, calling upstairs 'Bill, we have company.'

'Come through into the front room, lad,' mum said. 'Make yourself comfortable.' Then she went to make tea.

Johnny was a little surprised and asked Sheila if her mum was always that pale.

Sheila said, 'No. I hope she's all right.' She got up to go and see.

Then, dad burst into the room and gasped. He went pale too but quickly regained composure and colour, 'Hurry up with that tea Helen. This lad must be a nervous wreck.'

This was laughable really. Johnny was quite calm and obviously still wondered, like Sheila, why her parents had been so nervous. The visit went well, and so did the friendship. Later, when Johnny's talent earned him the title of Johnny Guitar and local fame and Sheila joined the Air Force, they remained firm friends.

Years later, now a mother herself, Sheila discovered from her mother, that she had a half brother named John who lived in Hetton-le-Hole and was five years older than her - the result of her father's wild oats period and had almost cost dad his freedom.

But that's another story.

*Johnny Moscardini was an astute businessman, he knew just what the teenagers in Horden needed; a place of their own to drink coffee or Coke and listen to the latest music on a Wurlitzer Jukebox, without parents, or any other disapproving eyes. A couple of booths for courting couples and an open area for those who were looking! Where, oh where, is his modern equivalent?*

# Chances Are

## Mavis Farrell

My name is Billy Winner. I am ten. My dad is called Brian and my mam, Sandra. We live up Canada, it's called that because its always cold and windy, but the real name is Holme Hill Estate.

My mam thinks my dad should be called Loser not Winner. She says he's a convulsive gambler because he goes in fits and starts. They shout at each other all the time especially when he borrows money out of her Benidorm jar and doesn't pay it back.

Me and my dad go up the Dog Track on Thursday nights and this particular night he really did win, honest! He borrowed a tenner from the Benidorm Jar when my mam was at the pictures with her friend Gloria, and he backed a five to one. It was great - just great!

I said, 'dad can we have a burger as well as chips tonight?'

And he said, 'Yes son, you can get me one as well.'

Well, I went out to the car park to the burger van and heard this terrible yelping. There was that Cruella Crow woman, the one who paints her lips like the Joker and has a face like a baboon's bottom. She was kicking hell out of a brindle greyhound, trying to get him into her van. It was terrible, the way she kept on, terrible, so I ran like mad to get my Dad.

My dad tried to stop her. He's a Hero, but she kicked the dog all the more. 'Don't you lay a finger on me, Brian Winner,' she said, 'or I'll have you up for assault,' she snarled. Then with a sly look she wheedled, 'I'll sell you the dog if you want. The price to you is sixty quid.'

She must have known we'd just won.

'Please dad, please buy him?' I begged. And she kicked the dog again, only harder this time.

My dad is a real Hero. He handed over all his winnings to Cruella. We didn't even get our burgers, we just took the dog home on a piece of string.

My mam went ape-shit, 'Fancy spending my Benidorm money on a useless dog,' she said. She refused to have him in the house - well both of them really, my dad and the dog. 'Go and live on your allotment at Withering Hope,' she said 'it's about all you're fit for, withering!'

It's really nice down the allotments you know. There's this man called Freddie who grows the heaviest leeks in the whole world. He's in the Guinness Book of Records you know, honest, and there's lots of other sound blokes. But you wouldn't want to live there, not in a leaking pigeon cree.

My dad stood his ground. He's a Hero.

'He's not going to live down the allotments,' he said, 'and neither am I. Come on Billy, we'll clean out the garden shed for the dog. I wonder what he's called?' We tried every name we could think of, but he just hung his poor miserable head. He only looked up when we said 'Dog' so we decided just to call him Dog. It was easier for him that way.

Me and my dad had to spend all our pocket money on food and flea powder, collar and leader and stuff like that, but it was worth it because Dog soon looked better and his lovely brindle coat didn't have bald patches any more. He still looked very sad. You have no idea how sad a dog can look unless you saw our Dog.

My mam would never let Dog in the house. 'I'm not having that lanky flea-ridden thing in here,' she said.

'But mam, he folds up very small,' I said.

'I have to consider my Dralon three piece and my Shag Pile,' she said. When my mam sniffs like that and stretches up as if she's tall you just know you're beat.

Dad didn't have any money to gamble with because of Dog's expenses, so he and mam got on a bit better. It was great at first, then they went all lovey-dovey. Yuk! I started to hope for a brother. I've always wanted a brother, but my mam said, 'No, I'm not going through that again. Once was enough. It's like having your body invaded by an alien.'

My dad says mam and Gloria watch too much Science Fiction.

Me and my dad started taking Dog out for long walks round the fields and Beacon Hill but Dog just trailed about. You'd think he'd be happy because we looked after him really well and loved him to bits.

'I think he's got depression,' dad said.

'Gran's got that,' I said, 'and she takes happy pills.'

After school on Tuesday I walked up the village to my gran and granda's. They live in the Ancient Miners' homes beside the council offices.

Don't old people have horrible habits? After his Sunday dinner my granda goes to bed. He takes his teeth out first and puts them on the kitchen window sill. They sit there and snarl, all covered in bits of cabbage and roast beef.

My gran's worse. She sits and picks at her horrible feet. 'You wouldn't want my bunions Billy,' she says.

'Too right gran,' I thought. The constant re-arranging of her corn plasters is like a work of art.

'Gran, could I possibly borrow a couple of your happy pills for Dog?' I said in my sweetest voice.

'No, I'm sorry Billy,' she said. 'I need them all for myself. No one knows what I have to put up with, what with your granda's prostrate and all that. He's up and down all night.'

So.... poor Dog just stayed depressed.

'Can we race him dad?' I said. 'It might cheer him up a bit.'

'Well,' dad said, 'theoretically we could. Easington Dogs is just a flapping track. You don't actually need a licence to race a dog there.' Dad sometimes uses these long words. 'But he'll have to go up for trials first to see if he's any good.'

We took Dog for trials that Sunday afternoon but he wouldn't even enter the trap. He just cried and shook and dug his stops in.

'That dog will never race,' the starter grumbled, 'been treated bad, probably.'

We took Dog home. I was gutted.

On Monday night a weird thing happened. There was this howling wind. It woke me and Dad but not my mam. She can sleep for England.

'Shall we see if Dog's all right?' I said, but the wind stopped as soon as it started so we just went back to bed.

Early next morning there was a pounding on the back door. 'Brian Winner! come out here, your garden shed is crushing my Brussels,' roared Moaning Maurice, our neighbour. Sure enough, Dog's shed was two doors down, smashed to pieces, devastating Maurice's vegetable garden.

'Where's Dog?' both me and my dad shouted together.

All that was left in our garden was the floor of Dog's shed. No sign of Dog. He was gone.

We found him up in the big field, running round and round and round like greased lightening. You could hardly see him, he was so fast.

'Wow!' we both said. 'Wow!'

After that we let Dog run whenever he felt like it and a sparkle came into his eyes and a spring into his step.

With Dog's shed being demolished my mam relented and let Dog live in the house. He really loved my mam and she secretly loved him back. He would lie beside her chair resting his chin on her fluffy pink slippers, gazing up at her while she pretended not to notice but secretly smiled. She stopped worrying about her shag pile.

We took Dog back for Sunday trials again and the starter let him have a run without going in the traps.

'He's caught the bloody hare!' shouted the starter. 'The electrics must have gone wrong.' But me and my dad knew better.

Eventually we got Dog into the trap but he hated it and despite his size, managed to turn in the trap so he faced the wrong way and missed the start of every trial. I was gutted at first but soon had a brilliant idea. 'Dad, if we put Dog in the trap back to front, he'll turn and be facing the right way for the start.'

'It's never been done before Billy lad,' he said. 'I doubt if it would work.'

It did work.' 'You can race your dog next Saturday,' the starter said, 'but he needs a track name. You can't enter him as *Dog.*'

We couldn't think of a good name. I was dead excited. My dad started to worry in case I would get too disappointed. 'You know Billy son, the chances are he might not win.'

'The chances are he *will* win dad, and that's his racing name, that's what we'll call him.....*Chances Are!*'

My dad lost a shift at the crisp factory on Wednesday. He went to a money-lender in Durham and borrowed a stash of cash. No one was supposed to know, especially not my mam. Dad gave all his mates and anyone else he could trust, twenty quid each to put on Dog as near to the start time as possible, something about...*not* shortening the odds. It was the biggest gamble of my dad's life. I worried all week in case Dog wouldn't turn in the trap on race night. Me and my dad didn't sleep.

Then the big night came. Dog, or should I say *Chances Are,* walked round as smart as a carrot, shining like silk. I was dead proud but everyone smirked and muttered when I put him in the trap back to front.

'The lad's gone crackers....shame. Smart dog though.'

I held my breath and my dad held his. He looked white as a sheet, well almost green. My dad's a Hero. I just felt sick.

'Well, *Chances Are* turned in the trap just in time and romped home, leaving the other five dogs standing. He actually created a record! Me and my dad were ecstatic, we jumped about and everybody cheered. It was great. Cruella Crow's face went purple as she screeched, 'That's my dog. I want him back!'

Everybody just laughed. It took dad ages to collect all our winnings and buy everybody a pint.

'Now that we're rich we can go to Benidorm for a whole fortnight, mam' I said much later when we got back home.

'I'm not that bothered Billy,' she said 'I don't want to leave Dog behind and he wouldn't be allowed on the plane you know.' She paused. 'And anyway, we're going to have a baby!'

F. Naughton

*Greyhound racing has been an important part of Easington's culture since Moorfield Stadium opened in 1934.*
*My Brother-in-law once owned a dog called 'Chances Are' and it did win...honest.*

# Gladiators

## Agnes Frain

Here come the Boys

The crowds converge as people jostle and shuffle their way through the turnstiles. Excitement crackles, our faces are alight with the hope that shines bright in our eyes. The hair on my neck shivers. I clamp my binoculars to my eyes and one by one I report to my husband the names of our team for today. Our anxious faces follow the movement of young, toned bodies as they run and swerve under the commands of their coach. Who is left out? Is this our best team?

Thousands of experts voice their opinion, freely, loudly - some scorn others praise. My husband tries to remove the binoculars from my neck, convinced I've been mistaken in naming today's gladiators. Gleefully I begin again.

Our striker is tall and powerful with braided black hair. Bouncing as he lopes like a gazelle, he covers the ground effortlessly. Who can mistake his partner, long and lean with a wide smile. Next, short legs pumping, shirt loose, comes a mid-fielder. He will create magic with his agile feet. He will baffle and bewilder.

Another - a giant - leaps as he heads the ball. He'll help build an impregnable wall; he's part of the shutter in front of goal. Another midfielder saunters past, curly dark hair and dark skin with a wonderful grace in his stride.

'They are so wrapped up I can't see their faces,' says my husband.

When I begin to point out the boys' individual body language - their posture, their strides, their different runs, even as to how they hold their arms, my husband snorts in disbelief.

Reluctantly, I surrender binoculars and settle down to resume my enjoyment. Anticipation is high. The seats are full. Then, with regret, I observe the players as they straggle across the field and disappear down the tunnel.

We climb to our seats, we nod and smile at the old lady, legs wrapped in a checked blanket, flask in hand. Eighty-plus, she's unfazed by the noise and bustle. She sits surrounded by strangers, smiles and greetings are given graciously. She beams - childlike - when tough young men pat her shoulder as they hasten to their seats.

Now the time is near, the formalities are over.

Music blasts, wonderful and uplifting.

As one entity we rise to our feet to pay homage to our boys.

*Our team.*

Surrounded by familiar faces, I take note of the boys who are now young men, tall and strong. These are the same boys who'd eagerly accepted gifts of sweets over the Christmas Seasons.

We are cocooned and safe here, all troubles put away: the power of the combined cheers will lift and support the individuals on the field who acknowledge the fans with upraised arms.

Among the crowd murmurs, whispers, gather momentum as the famous faces of the opposition are spotted. Who cares about flasher players? They are not ours. They're just interlopers we have to tolerate.

Lift your heads boys! This is your day, your home. We greet you with roars of encouragement. Applause and chants will give you wings. You will dance and twirl and brush off the thundering feet and outstretched boots.

Today you will be our heroes. Our gladiators.

# Waiting In the Dark

## Mary N. Bell

Crouching behind the bushes - hiding.

Two hours I have been waiting here. Watching, and waiting, making my mind up. I kept out of sight because I wanted no one to see me. That's why I'm dressed in a dark coat and hood. I crept through the colliery, hoping no one would recognise me with the hood pulled down over my face and a bulky jacket hiding my shape. I am well known in this pit village.

I creep past the shops - Ferry's the Chemists, then the paper shop with a poster in the window advertising the evening paper. Not many people about. It is so bitterly cold with the wind from the North Sea blowing through the streets.

The temperature is dropping on this January day. It is dusk now, the lights have come on and the sea beyond the steep cliffs reflects the dark clouds as they roll over the winter sky like curtains closing yesterday off.

Funny how no one has committed suicide by drowning in our sea. I wouldn't do that; the sea is my friend. Listen to it as it rolls to the shore – shshsh – shshsh – shsh, whispering its secrets as it rolls up the beach. I can swim.

In the next village they jump off the viaduct but here it is the railway line, instant and I hope pain-free. Suddenly, I realise I can't feel my toes or finger ends. They are stiff with the cold. I'm determined not to give up my intention. Should I go home? My house would soon warm up. I switched the heating off when I left home what seemed like hours ago.

I'm not going to give up now watching and waiting.

My house would be warm and cosy in 10 minutes, I am staying here behind the bushes. Here is another one, the noise like thunder. Why am I here? Think. What was life about? Making money, spending it, getting up, going to bed.

Better to have loved and lost than never to have loved at all. That old saying is not true. To have loved, lost and been discarded, that was humiliation. Where have I gone wrong? What have I done wrong? The worst part, he made love to me, then said 'I'm seeing someone else.' An explosion rocketed in my head, feeling as though my head was being blown into a million pieces. He carried on, 'That's why I've been leaving you early at night. She's been waiting for me.'

'Who is she?' That didn't really matter to me. I was nice looking and I had a good job, had my own house and car, and was that not enough?

'Dolly Jones,' he said.

'Her? She's scum. Her brothers are in prison for drug dealing. You prefer her to me?' I asked hardly able to breathe for the pain in my chest. Was my heart breaking?

'I love her. She's waiting for me now I have to go.'

And so he went.

That's why I'm here hiding behind the bushes so no one can see me. Waiting for courage waiting for the right time. Waiting for the right train.

# Lost In Witches' Copse

## Ann Peel

'Coming, ready or not!' Katie called and began her search in the field behind the stables and old house. She could see the roofs of Grant's Houses just over the rise. This was a great game, in the fields behind Horden Hall, just beside Paul's home on the path to Thorpe Dene. She and Tina lived on the estate across Thorpe Road. Their weekend treat was to come and play near to Paul's home. There were so many good hiding places, lots of hedges, bushes and outbuildings, all of which added together to make hide and seek their favourite game.

As she followed the hedge she thought to herself that it was too open here, nowhere to hide, no long grass and the rapeseed was hardly ankle high. It would grow quickly but was at present a hopeless hiding place. Just ahead was the bunch of trees that her mam had told her was called Witches' Copse. Katie hesitated but thought to herself that Paul would choose it to hide in. He was a year older and very brave, such a scary place wouldn't worry him.

She stepped into Witches' Copse and examined her surroundings, aware that Paul might be behind the very next tree. Of course he wasn't but she looked for him anyway. The hairs on her neck stood to attention. There was no sound, not a bird, not a rabbit, no field mouse or hedgehog or any other animal, not even a breath of wind and there was always a wind off the North Sea. She was very nervous and suddenly aware that not even Paul, with all his bravado, was here, only small, scared, Katie. She carried on moving to the centre of the copse where she found........emptiness. No trees. She looked up into a perfect circle of sky, a beautiful blue with a few, small fluffy clouds but it looked ominous, threatening, like a large creature awaiting its prey. Katie had never felt so completely alone and vulnerable. Now she really wished that Paul *was* behind the next tree. How strange, there was no middle, it was like a big tree doughnut and she was stuck in its dead centre.

Katie began to run straight ahead, not looking anywhere but where she was going, determined to stop for nothing.

Her heart was beating double-time; her brain ran at the same pace. Was it excitement or fear that had caused this panic? Could this be fear?' she thought and picked up speed, still looking only straight ahead, determined to get out of here as fast as she could. She had no reason for fear, it was just a wood, an odd wood, no trees in the middle, but just a wood. Where were Paul and Tina, why couldn't she find them?

The silence was so profound it was unnerving, not even the traffic that she knew must be passing along the Coast Road and Thorpe Road interrupted this silence. She'd had enough and screamed at the top of her voice. 'Paul, Tina, where are you?' Silence, her shout made this more obvious and she increased her speed, muttering, 'Just a small wood, I'll be out in a few seconds.' She ran for what seemed forever, it felt like a silent movie, a horror, silent movie and she would never escape! Close to tears, Katie refused to cry, well she might once she got out of this awful place and could breathe free air again and see her friends and smell the grass instead of her own sweat and this awful nightmare would end.

In a breath she could hear the traffic and the voices of Tina and Paul calling her name. 'I'm here,' she shouted with relief. 'Yes, I am here aren't I,' she said, touching her cheeks and arms, just to be sure. She looked around and found that she was at the same point as she had entered the copse, how strange. She was so sure that she had run in a straight line and should be on the Thorpe Road side, behind that empty bungalow. Shaking her head she walked to where Paul and Tina were waiting on the path near his home. Also his mam, Tina's mam, and her own mam....What was going on?

Her mam raced forward, held Katie close and said, 'Where have you been all this time, we've looked everywhere for you?'

'What do you mean, mam, haven't been anywhere. We were playing hide and seek and it was my turn to be on, I was just looking for the other two!'

'For three hours,' screamed mam, 'I have been demented looking for you since Paul told his mum that they couldn't find you.'

Katie was shocked, 'Three hours, it was never that long!'

'Where were you Katie?' Paul asked. 'We looked everywhere, even knocked at Horden Hall and searched the stables! You must have found the best hiding place ever!'

'I went into the copse because I thought you were there,' she said.

Paul shuddered. 'Me? Go in there, never. I tried once and it scared me to death, never again!'

Katie and her mam called into grandma's house on their way home, to let her know Katie was safe. After Katie told her tale, grandma grimaced and said, 'That's where the witches' coven used to meet, from way back. There had always been a coven. My mam told me all about it. I remember her saying how glad she was that I was born on the 26th of October because if I'd waited five more days they might have stolen me for their black magic.' 'Oh, grandma,' laughed Katie. 'It was an adventure and very scary, but the only black magic involved is your chocolates.'

F. Naughton

# The Darkness Within

## Terry Dobson

It started to rain, a heavy downpour that matched my mood. The clouds were grey and oppressive and I felt that they were pressing down upon me. The wind howled, a harsh taskmaster that whipped up the waves into a frenzy as they assaulted the pebbled beach. There was a darkness inside me that hammered at my ribcage like a prisoner desperate for freedom. I took deep breaths as I fought against it. I couldn't let it out, not yet. Now wasn't the time.

I choked it down.

She was gone, and without her my life was as ripped apart as her body had been. I could still see her blood as it dripped red from the ceiling and oozed down the walls. Whenever I thought of her I would always see it, the horror and brutality, and that was the most painful of all. Our love, our lives together, our laughter, our joy, and all the happy times I should remember had been overpowered, overshadowed and suffocated by the annihilation of it all.

I turned to walk along the beach banks towards Beacon Hill and pushed forward against the oncoming northerly wind. Rain lashed at my face. There was a flash of lightning and there, at the summit, I thought I caught a glimpse of something; a silhouette with wings. I brushed the water from my eyes to see more clearly and peered through the torrent, but there was nothing. Whatever it had been, if there had been anything, it was gone. I was alone once again with the storm and my grief.

I carried on walking, steps leaden and the mud sucking greedily at my shoes, lost in my thoughts and memories. Suddenly, from behind me, I heard a flapping, thrumming noise, like tent canvas in the wind, getting closer and louder. Instinctively I ducked, and felt a chill as something skimmed past me. I looked up and saw it, a creature of evil, night-shadow black, ethereal, with viciously sharp obsidian claws and leathery wings.

I clenched my fists, closed my eyes and raised my head to the blackened sky while water cascaded down my face. The creature swooped again and turned towards me, talons outstretched, with a mocking challenge in its piercing shriek. I opened my mouth and cried out in reply, giving voice to everything I was feeling - a long terrible sound of intense rage and torment.

I woke with a scream as I lashed out, drenched in a cold sweat and tangled in my sheets. My heart raced. I shivered and took some deep breaths in an attempt to regain some calm. It had been a dream then. I shook my head. No, it was more than that; one of my visions. I pulled free of the sheets and stood.

I crossed the room and stared into the mirror. I was still trembling. My face was pale and damp. Something was coming, something bad, and I didn't know whether I was ready.

# Ritual of the Dance

## Susan Robinson

It's Halloween, Night of the Dark Angel and his cronies, when the veil between the realms of light and shade is lifted. Witches, vampires, and ghouls gather in the shadows. Some brave persecution and knock on doors of strangers to beg for treats. Others meet at feasts where they, like gluttons who haven't fed for ages, gorge on such delights of food and drink to last them until next year. It's a time for spells and rituals; for mischief, magik and mayhem; and for divination.

Her parents dress up to take part. It takes hours to change the shape of their faces with false skin stuck on with gum arabic then whitened with stage makeup. They glue fangs over their own teeth with special putty so they look like grotesque vampires. Melissa, their daughter, has real fangs of her own, small neat incisors like snakes have, with hollow tubes but hers are for drawing energy in, not for spitting venom out; although she can do this if provoked. She has the pale skin and the long black hair of a modern day vampire. It's as if she doesn't belong to her family. In olden times she might have been identified as a changeling child. But Melissa is no changeling child, no snivelling, wizened fairy child. She has the blood of the real vampyr – a most magical practitioner - in her veins. But she is an only, lonely child and tonight she has a plan. The opportunity the Hallows Eve brings will not be missed. Tonight she seeks a sister, one just like her.

'Come on, Melissa. Hurry up, we'll be late.' Her mother screeches at her as they traipse up the hill to the new estate behind The Welfare. Each side of the street is studded with white houses that glimmer like field mushrooms under the full moon. Monsters of all persuasions have taken over the land. Every house they pass spits out more. They all head for a gap in the fence that surrounds the cricket pitch in the park directly behind the estate. The Feast of All Hallows has begun.

Bar-B-Q beef roast and hot-dog and onion smells scribble the air. A misplaced bonfire scorches the hallowed pitch and burns any disguised face that comes too close; greasepaint melts and plastic masks stick to sweaty brows. Fireworks shriek and pierce the night to send their ghost sounds into the ether. The adult festival-goers group together in a beer tent to take part in the mandatory drink ritual. Their offspring are left to their own devices. Twenty or so gruesome kids make a beeline for Melissa who stands on her own away from the crowd.

'Weirdo,' they chant.

'Goblin,' is the whisper.

'Pull her fangs off. Yank her teeth out,' they sing as they dance a bizarre hop and skip in a ring around her. They pull ugly faces and wave hideous hands in her direction.

Melissa circles round looking at each child in turn; she begins to swirl faster and faster. She doesn't speak. Her long hair streaks horizontally, her arms outstretch while her fingers appear to grow so as to touch her tormentors. A malicious wind coils around the dancers, to sting arms and legs with bonfire sparks. The kids appear not to notice, and dance as if spell-bound. Costumes singe and smells of scorched cloth pinch the nose.

She stops.

Around her the dance goes on. The children's feet blister the earth. Trails of smoke prance and waver. She lifts her hand. The dance slows.

'Come.' Her voice hums and echoes. Its low moan vibrates the air, like far-away thunder.  Out of the corner of her eye she sees unformed figures begin to materialise out of the gloom beyond the light of the bonfire.

The shadows deepen. The invisible starts to become more visible. The children follow her like a grisly rat's tail as she steps into the night and then down the tree path to the crossroads in the park where the oak stands. Naked branches knot together, black against the moon-struck sky. The kids hold hands to ring the tree and as they spiral round it the energy of the dance picks up - faster and faster they go like the devil is after them. They stir the wind to fever pitch. It howls like a banshee. Tree-tops thrash and groan.

Melissa stands, arms raised to the fury. 'Come my grandfathers. Bring me my sister. Take these children. Take their energy. Now is the time.'

With a noise like feral cats screaming, the night tears itself into a powerful storm, and lightning cracks open the darkness to release a fearful procession of vampyric spirits.

The Wild Hunt rides.

Melissa has summoned the ancestors.

Pale ghosts of vampires wreathe around the tree to join the dance macabre.  Witches and dark deities merge into the circle. Skeletal fingers grasp warm hands. The dance speeds up. Feet are lifted into the air, higher and higher. Everything becomes a blur. The visible becomes invisible. A violent crash fills the air. The ground shakes, then all is still. Of the children there is no sign. A slight sulphuric smoke whispers from the tree's trunk beside which stands a child.

Ashen but unafraid she holds out her hand.

Melissa reaches out to her and smiles a sisterly smile.

As they walk away, they look back. On the tree, in fractures in the bark are little crosses made of straw – about twenty if someone was to stop and count. Melissa nods her head in satisfaction, after all she's not unkind and remembrances should be made of her sister's birthplace.

# The Doctor's Wife

## Susan Robinson

I was ten when Mam died of TB
And left us on our own
With an uncle we called dad
Seven kids, five of his
And me and a lad
Off the brother
Who was dead, time I was three.

The doctors kept Mam's baby
And took her off to Texas
I never saw her
Dr Barnado's took
Two smaller kids to London
While two more, bigger
Were shipped to Portsmouth forever.

The lad came back
From an aunt that could do
Nothing with him
And I was between the Minister
And the Doctor's wife
For what could be seen
As the highest bidder.

I was tired of being
A Mam to all of them
Of drudgery and chores
And of having nothing much
Just sometimes getting sixpence
When the uncles did their singing
On a Sunday after dinner

I didn't go to school
The College On The Move came to me
But I still couldn't read
About Christopher Robin
In a book in the room I got
At the Doctor's wife's
Who won my lottery.

I called *her* Mam
Right away
I used to pick her white flowers
She'd lost the Doctor and their son
And had no-one
Just memories of what might have been
As well as a miscarriage.

She adopted me – officially
A little three stone kid
Who couldn't see to serve
Over the counter at her shop
Where I went to live
By myself
Just the Doctor's wife and me.

*This poem is based on truth.*
*They do say that truth is stranger than fiction, although families were split up like this then*
*before social services had any input – see also the story*
*Jimmy Cagney Was My Hero.*

# Bus War 1

Ann Peel

I bet they live somewhere else, never rode beside me
A change of number and a slight change of route
Said the men from the bus company
To save a few corners and money for them
At the expense of my legs don't you see.
How would they feel if we all walked away
And the route became passenger free?
Our community centre's closed now
So the Welfare's where I want to be
But your bus doesn't go there anymore,
Fighting back is the obvious key
What use is a free transport pass
If you can't get where you want to be.
So let's ask the Council for money instead
Or a taxi service that's free
Lets veto the bus route my dears
Petitions don't work don't you see
A bus service is meant to be just that
A service to you and to me
So we chose the competitor's bus
And your driver was no busy bee
There was no one to pick up, nobody to drop
Within weeks the old route was back, gee!
Next time you want to change the route
Ask the old people who use it you see
We won't charge you thousands for changing your mind
Our service, like yours will be free.
Yes free to go where we want
Free to us.... you get paid a fee
We worked all our lives to earn our free rides
Fares are gratis to retired ones like me.

# Bus War 2

## Ann Peel

We now have our bus service back
But there is still something wrong it is true
The one stop that most of us want it to make
Is the one that the bus cannot do.
Eden Street is the thorn in our sides,
The Post Office pension day curse
By the time we've collected our money you see
We go home with a really full purse
To walk from South Terrace or the Victory Club
Is really an awful long way
If you're old and your legs tire easily,
Then you have to limit your stay
I am sure that Horden businesses
Are about to go seriously broke
Cos we don't all drive cars and we aren't all young
And shopping on foot is no joke
Durham Council this time are to blame
Altering Horden without thinking first
A simple bus stop in Eden Street
Would solve the problem that's worst.
Car drivers are selfish you see,
Have to park right where they want to be
Just a little more thought and a slight further walk
Then the bus could stop too don't you see
Parking legally helps too, you know,
Not both sides of the road....corners free
So the bus can follow its route
And drop off the oldies like me.

# Innocence

## Agnes Frain

It had been a stressful week. The rain, spiteful and constant with little respite, had pounded the woods for days. Thick mud clung to the thin boots of the timber cutters as they struggled to keep upright. Thin felt hats drooped beneath the weight of water. The men cursed when a waterfall flowed down their backs, their bowed shoulders only protected from the elements with sacks stolen from the grain sheds.

Gabriel laboured close to his brother Ralf for protection. The other wood -cutters were uptight and impatient: they needed a scapegoat. Their faces were pinched and tight, filled with anxiety.

Bemused, during the short meal breaks, Gabriel listened to their complaints. They ranted about this constant rush for timber. They fretted about the spreading railway tracks. Why was their employer, the local land- owner, stripping the woods and not replanting? Why was this year different? During bad weather, they usually worked around the farm buildings, but Mr Hartley had yelled for more trees to be felled, in spite of the dangerous conditions.

Their complaints came thick and fast. Were they going to be cast aside? Would they have to join the throng of men begging for a job at the newly sunk mines of Hetton and Haswell? Would they be forced to become men who emerged from the underground blinking in the daylight, with blackened bodies and stooped backs - miners who coughed and spat out black dust then breathed deep, searching for fresh air?

All this talk confused Gabriel. His wide flattened face and vacant eyes showed little animation. Hemmed in by men like mature trees he couldn't grasp why they were so angry. He retreated into his own world, away from anger. He dreamed and hummed a monotonous tune.

As darkness fell, the brothers escaped from the soaked wood to their small tied cottages. Lit by oil lamps, with wet clothes hanging in front of the fire in a fruitless hope of drying, Ralf's small cottage was a dismal place.

Gabriel kept his eyes downcast, during the family meal. Ann, Ralf's wife, sat with her hands clasped in her lap. Her spiteful darting eyes made Gabriel squirm. Her husband and father-in-law shovelled their food into their mouths. Ann spat out spiteful words about the lack of Grace before their meal: God should be thanked for the food. They could eat if they liked, but she refused to eat anything that had not been blessed.

Ralf exploded. 'It was the sweat of our labour: food not God.'

'Don't you realise this food could be taken from our mouths?' said his father.

Ralf, frustrated, threw his food at the wall and raged at his pious wife, harsh words poured from his mouth. 'Haven't you heard the rumour of strangers coming to strip the woods? We'll have to labour for a pittance. We'll be thrown from the cottage just to satisfy the greed of Mr Hartley. We'll be like the rest of those helpless fools, bowing to the new master, King Coal.'

Feeling unable to grasp all this serious stuff, Gabriel clambered into his musty bed, desperate to hide under his thin blankets. He burrowed down the bed and began his humming. Raised voices talking about killing their heartless boss sent him into a restless sleep, into nightmares of killing with his own strong hands this enemy of his family.

The next morning the rain had begun to ease. Gabriel lumbered ahead of the other workers as they straggled towards the woods. He stretched his long arms and placed a parcel across two branches in the crooked oak tree. Then, chopping and trimming, he drifted through the morning until renewed torrential rain soaked his clothes. Running with the workers to the shack for shelter, he slipped in the dense mud.

Curses from the other men echoed around him as he struggled to his feet. They feared they would soon be driven back into the downpour if the boss snooped around.

Their words halted Gabriel's dash. The nightmare resurfaced, but this time he was ready. Sneaking away, he rescued the parcel. Now the contents - his grandfather's old musket - rested near his racing heart.

Noises. Ralf was calling. Gabriel ducked further under the tree, blending into the bark. He peered through the close-knit trunks, watching the rain as it bounced and spun from sodden leaves. Shaking his head, he wiped wetness away from his forehead with his thick fingers, and then flicked it away.

He began to hum; he stood there in a dream-like state. He struggled to focus, to catch fragmented memories. He strove to recollect why he was standing here, under this tree.

Where were Ralf and the other workers? Raising his head, he could see the sky had cast off its darkness and the rain had stopped. Fingers of light spread across the sky. Gabriel gave a cry of pleasure as part of a rainbow illuminated the woods.

Then, nearby, the snap of a twig alerted him. Gasping in fright he fought to regain his scattered wits. A tall warmly-clad man strode towards him. The landowner's heavy boots floated over the mud; his head was covered in a broad-brimmed hat. Swinging a heavy cane, Mr Hartley waited as the workers began to return to their tasks.

Pointing to a pile of new timber, the master pulled out his gold pocket watch. His manner was aggressive. Raising his voice, he berated the men. Their excuses fell on deaf ears; he leaned on his stick and his plump body oozed indifference.

That was when, nudged into action, standing with the musket pressed against his shoulder, Gabriel began to act out his night terrors.

This was his family's enemy. His eyes widened and he pulled the trigger. There was a flash followed by a loud boom and then pungent smoke choked him. The force of the shot caused the musket to rebound and slam into his shoulder. He dropped the weapon, gasping in pain and then clasped his hands over his ringing ear. Gabriel sank to the mud. In panic he clawed at the undergrowth, desperate to find a place where he could vanish into the sodden root-covered earth.

In the trunk of a small oak tree to the right of Mr Hartley was a large misshapen hole. Smoke drifted into the air as workers scattered, shouting that poachers must be about. The intended victim spluttered with outrage, screaming threats at the supposed poachers.

At that moment a mighty roll of thunder echoed through the woods. Lightning flashed from the sky and struck a branch that cracked and sizzled. Curled into a ball, Gabriel moaned in terror as the rain returned with a vengeance. Was this the wrath of God?

Mr Hartley raged at the workers who had come back empty-handed from their search of the woods. The exhausted men were ordered to return to their homes. He would expect them to be bright and early the next day. With threats of further action if the poacher returned to his land, the landowner stalked away.

Blackness. Gabriel stayed, pressed against the trunk of the twisted oak, unable to move, still numb with the folly of his deed. He was alone. Ralf was gone. He pinched himself; he knew this was not a dream. This was the here and now. Rocking, arms clasped about his cold body, he began to hum.

Then the blaring sound of a screech owl overhead sent him into a shuddering frenzy. He collapsed face down onto the rank soil, taking in the stink of urine mixed with the smell of his vomit. The smell of his own sweat joined the smell of wet roots and leaves, wild garlic clung to his clothes.

He heard urgent whispers, then saw a lighted flare weaving its way through the trees. More horror. Was he in the fires of hell? He crawled to the trunk of his shelter and forced his weakened legs upright. Tears flowed down his filthy face, his lips trembled and he began to wheeze.

Then loving arms were reaching for him and his father took the musket and comforted him with words of love. When he had calmed down Ralf led him to the small oak and pushed Gabriel's fingers into the burnt twisted oak where the musket ball nestled. 'You did it, Gabriel. You did it. You had the courage.'

Then the child-like man, still in shock, stumbled after his rescuers. They came to the tumbling beck and, holding the musket aloft, his father hurled the weapon into a watery grave.

'Now,' said Ralf. 'It's time to go home, Gabriel.'

*During the conversion of my niece's loft, when the beams were replaced with steel supports, a musket ball was discovered buried deep in one of the beams. Following a visit to the Durham Light Infantry Museum we established that the last musket rifle was in use in 1837. Further research revealed that before the mines were sunk in East Durham the countryside was covered in farms and woodland. This inspired my story of how the musket ball came to be buried in the oak.*

# Great Uncle Bert

## Joan Wright

Get yourself out of bed
Ma was angry, face red
I want you down here and fast
But Ma, I've a pain
From my toes to my brain
Very soon I'll be breathing my last
It's cos Great Uncle Bert
That incurable flirt
Is here on a visit, our Mabel
Just come down and say
You feel frisky today
And let him chase you round the table
He's cuddled our Grace
Though she spat in his face
And Bessie escaped up a tree
The ladder he got
But climb it could not
He forgets that he's now ninety three
Our Amy surrendered
I thought she was splendid
She let him give her a 'chaste' kiss
I mean that he chased her
Round the garden he raced her

Til she gave him his moment of bliss
Now he's grabbed our Gert
Oooh she's playing the flirt
And enjoying the slap and the tickle
I won't dare tell your dad
He'd go raving mad
And then she would be in a pickle
He's outside again
And it's starting to rain
Our Bessie is still up the tree
What could be more madder
He's climbing the ladder
Oh he's fallen, I better go see

Oh you're up our Mabel
No chase round the table
He's just had a heck of a spill
Split open his head
And he's now very dead
I wonder if he's made a will.

# Pitman Beware

Mary N. Bell

I dominate this place and you revolve around me
Mesmerised hypnotised you are drawn to see
If I am a dream or a constant nightmare
It is no hallucination, I am there.
Step into my cage at the ring of a bell
Plummet through the earth to a special hell
If I wish I'll do you harm
I'll break a limb, a leg, an arm
Respect me or I'll take your life
Make your child an orphan, a widow your wife
Breathe in my stench gasses and dust
Dig and get coal from my seams if you must
But pitman beware you have one life to lose
And I will take it whenever I choose.

# Retribution

## Susan Robinson

I see him at the bottom of the cemetery bank opposite The Black Diamond. I tell the child to hurry and push my wheelchair around the corner out of sight into Withering Hope where the allotment association hut is. My heart pounds. I want to get up and run but this damned sickness has my life.

'Mam?'

'Shush Kathy, pet.'

I feel like I'm drowning. I scarcely breathe, not daring to gasp my terror in case he hears. With any luck he didn't see us. But immediately his black-clad figure's right in front of me like a spectre. His pulpit voice intones the thunder of God. I shrink from its power.

*'Vengeance is mine, sayeth the Lord. He has visited upon you just retribution.'*

White noise fills my head. The silent screaming that began when I was twelve gets louder and louder until when I open my mouth the howling starts.

I feel our Kathy stroke my hands. She's always done this to calm me when I get agitated. This time I push her hands away. She can't hold my hand. I won't let her. I flail the air and slap at her touch. The edges of my vision are blurred. His face hovers like an apparition from the devil, cut off at the neck by the white band that signifies his calling.

*'Atone for your sin. God is merciful. Repent... repent... rep...'*

'...Mam... mammy! Are you alright, mammy? Shall I run and get dad?'

Her voice trembles with tears. It's been a nasty one this time, the worst for quite a few months. I thought perhaps with the new medication off the doctor these attacks might be over. I'm exhausted. 'Take me home, pet. Let's not tell dad, eh?'

'Jennifer!' Mam's voice followed me out of our house on the colliery farm. 'Jenny, pick our Brian up from the church after your jazz band practice, will you?'

I pop my head round the back door. 'Aw, mam. Do I have to? I don't like the Father. He's scary.'

'Look, it's not far out of your way and you know our Brian doesn't like coming across the pit yard in the dark. And watch what you say about the Father or you'll be saying it at confession. Give him a chance. He's only new, you'll get used to him.'

I'm a good girl, me, but I sometimes speak without thinking. But God knows what I'm thinking anyway, so I might as well say it is my reasoning. I wish I was more holy like my friend Christiana. She was born on Christmas day and wants to be a nun when she grows up. I mean how holy is that? I don't want to be a nun; I want to be like my mam. People say I look just like her, and she's pretty with her black hair and violet eyes - just like Elizabeth Taylor – so that's something anyway.

I love the jazz band – Easington Emeralds – and the green and white satin costumes. I'm the drum majorette and with practice I might get to be lead majorette, but Sally Kirby can throw and twirl better than me, so she's at the front – for now. The time always flies by and as usual I'm late as I leave the white hut behind the shops in Seaside Lane to run down the now empty streets – the straight line of Ashton Street, round the pay office then along the east side of never-ending Station Road past the Trust and it's beery smell down towards the Church. I don't like the dark either, so I hurry between the street lights that shine just a little way in the black night like the torch the woman at the pictures uses. Frost patterns appear on the pavement under the cones of light. I squint my eyes and the ice turns into diamonds. I listen for footsteps, scared in case I hear them, and scared in case I don't.

I stop outside the Church at the Grotto of Our Lady. It's like a stone cave and inside it is a statue of Her. Oh, she's lovely is Our Lady. I do a little curtsey and cross myself. I try to put my face to look like Hers – all holy and kind. But it's no use – I'm just me.

Inside the Church all is quiet. I'm really late. I can't hear anyone, our Brian must have gone. I'll get wrong off mam for sure. I'll have to catch him up. I turn to go. Then I hear a noise, a mewling sound from the vestry. The door's slightly open. It must be the church cat. It's kept to get the rats that come off Foxholes Dene, but it shouldn't be in the vestry in case it pees. I'll do the Father a favour and put it outside. It'll be my good turn for him, even though I don't like him. Perhaps I'll get some holy points off God.

I peer around the door. The light is dim and for a moment I can't see anything but the choir's clothing hung on pegs around the room. But there, in the corner, kneels the Father. He has his back to me and can't see that I look. In front of him almost hidden in the folds of clothing is our Brian. The Father has his hands on my brother's body, it looks like he's helping our Brian put on his coat but I see that he strokes and feels. His hands touch where they shouldn't. Our Brian has his eyes closed but there's fear on his face. I know this isn't right. I don't know what to do. My legs feel like water and I'm frightened. Then the Father kisses our Brian. On his lips. It's not a holy kiss. It's not the kind of kiss that our dad gives.

It's the devil's kiss.

'Get off him. Leave him alone.' I stumble into the room and grab our Brian by the arm. 'Come on, we'll get wrong off mam.'

The Father gets to his feet. He makes the sign of the cross over our Brian, as if that's what he was doing all the time. He doesn't fool me. I just knew there was something scary about him. What if he's really the devil?

'You're a nasty man, Father. Wait till I tell me dad.'

'And just what will you tell your dad, Jennifer? That you saw me, the priest give a blessing to your brother? For that's what it was, and Brian will vouch for me, won't you Brian?'

'Our Brian's only nine, he's just a bairn and he's scared of you. I know what I saw and I'll tell, I will.'

The Father moves away from us to stand by the door, and blocks our way out. '*Telling lies is a sin Jennifer. God will punish you. You don't want that, do you?* Look, you were mistaken. The light in here is low. I'll understand. You won't need to come to confession. I forgive you.'

Our Brian is crying. 'Let's go home, Jenny. I want me mam. I've wet myself.'

'You're a horrible person, Father. It's not me telling lies. I'm a good girl.'

'Repent before it's too late and I shall pray for you.'

He reaches out to place his hand on my head. I take this chance. I kick him hard on the shins and we duck under his outstretched arm out of the door and run as fast as we can out of the church and into the street.

Some men come out of The Trust. They bring the smell of the pub with them on hot breath that clouds out of them like smoke. They're strangers. We run down East to the pit wall and then along it where empty colliery street after colliery street stretch from it at right angles like lonely pews in a ruined church. Everyone's behind lit curtained windows, having their supper or watching the tele. We turn into Office Street and as we do I look back. There some distance behind is The Father, silhouetted by a cold moonlight that shines a frosty glare on slate roofs.

'Wait,' I hear him call.

'Oh God. He's coming after us. Run, Brian, run.'

Once through the pit gates into the yard I pull Brian into the cover of a building to catch our breath. The bairn's sobbing. I put my arm around him.

'It wasn't my fault, Jenny. He said God wanted me to let him. He said it would make me special.'

'I know, don't worry pet. Me dad'll sort it.'

Brian starts to wail. 'Don't tell me dad. The Father said not to, said God would know and I'd be sent to Hell.'

He twists away from me and runs out into the part of the pit yard where we're not supposed to go, away from the path that leads us home. I follow him. The pit yard is lit with huge lights that throw heavy black shapes on the ground. I see our Brian's shadow stretch towards the tunnel under the railway lines where the pit ponies go. The skeleton outline of the aerial flight strides overhead, its buckets of waste clank and groan like the ghost train at the fair. I see the long shape of The Father's shadow as it falls in front of me. He's not far behind. My breath hurts my chest like the cough I had last winter. I trip and stumble to the tunnel entrance where out of the range of the lights all is dark, darker than black.

'Brian... Brian!' I hear that mewling noise again. 'Brian, answer me.'

'Jen...nn...ny.'

I almost fall over him, huddled as he is where the tunnel leads out to the pony field. I grab hold of him. 'He's still after us. We must get home. Come on, up the field. We'll cross the lines near the farm.'

'We can't go near the lines Jenny, me dad'll go mad.'

'We have no choice. Hurry.'

I hold his hand. We run, our feet slipping on the uneven ground, our breath raw in our throats. Up ahead I see the lights of the farm and of our house where my mam will be worried sick wondering where we are. I look back. The Father is nearer than I thought. I can hear him. Then I see him. He looks like a mad black vampire with the moonlight behind him that lights up a pathway on the sea. He screeches when he sees us.

'*Stop, ye devil's spawn. Repent! The wrath of God will be upon you.*'

We reach a place where the embankment is low. I scramble through the brambles at the edge dragging our Brian after me. The railway lines shine like silver hair-ribbons. I hear a slight humming noise coming from them. I step over the first line. In my head I hear my dad say to be careful. 'Come on Brian, we're nearly there.' I tug and tug on his hand.

Brian screams like a rabbit caught by a dog. 'He's got me, Jenny. He's got me.'

'Pull away from him, Brian. Pull.' I yank harder on our Brian's hand with both of my hands. 'Get off him, you blasted bugger. Leave us alone.' I yell into the night. It's a tug of war.

'*Lead us not into Temptation. Deliver us from Evil.*'

'Help, Jenny. Help me.'

I haul myself over the next line and heave for all I'm worth. I still have hold of our Brian's hand. He's still with me. But I can feel the Devil pulling on his other arm.

'*God will visit upon you just retribution. Atone....atone...*' His voice is like thunder pounding its power into the darkness.

I don't hear the train. I still hold our Brian's hand. White noise fills my head. The silent screaming begins.

# What Lies Beneath

## Agnes Frain

Benches strewn with damp towels
Chloride pungent catching your breath
Garish colours clash
Murky water filled with a rainbow
Rubber caps bobbing between line marking flags
Clatter of wooden doors rebound
Primitive changing room in constant use

Multiple propelled bodies thrash their arms
Triumphant shouts and quiet tears
Teenagers preening in a secluded corner
Elasticised swimsuits emphasise curves
Matrons knitting quack like ducks
Tight perms nod at the latest slander
Brave divers bow at cat-calls and applause

*All things bright and beautiful*

Lurking in a corner pretending to read
Towel draped casually across his lap
Sly looks with hooded eyes
Licked fat lips and soft white hands
Approached by a father broad and strong
Dragging his towel, he is hustled away
Childless he came and childless he departs.

*Horden Resevoir was popular until the mid sixties but always, despite the laughter and splashing,
it seemed to hold hidden secrets. The sides of the reservoir were green and slimy and it was difficult to keep a foothold.
The water was sometimes covered in tiny flies.*

# The Last Supper

## Ann Peel

Paul prepared to start the evening - notepads to the ready, his uniform clean and pressed, highly polished black shoes. Last but not least he put on an ingratiating smile of welcome for the group as they approached the table that he was to attend for their meal at Hardwick Hall - a few hours of pleasure for them and a final night of serfdom for him.

This was Paul's last Saturday evening working here. On Monday he began his new job. He would no longer need to work evenings to subsidise his student allowance. He watched as each member took his or her place at the refectory style table. One by one he gave them their menu.

Tom, the Head of Council opened the proceedings. 'Well colleagues, our last official meal. You might say it's quite an occasion. Lets sort out the menu before we go any further.'

This was Tom's usual watering hole. He knew exactly what his choice would be. His girth more or less chose his food for him, paté followed by a huge T-Bone.

He sat back and examined the people around him, seeing his working life around the table. Beside him, his P. A., Stephen, a tall elegant young man who had no intention, for once in his life, of considering the prices on the menu. Bitter thoughts were coursing through his mind. *All my career has been dedicated to this Council and now they pull the rug from under our feet, I'll make sure this last meal is the one I enjoy most.* He chose prawn cocktail and Salmon En Croute. Fish had always been his favourite and tonight he intended to enjoy it.

The Financial Director, Alan, frowned at the menu, his broad shoulders, sagging slightly. *This diet will be the death of me, but I really can't afford to take a chance.* So he chose melon with raspberry sauce and roast chicken without sauce. His dour face was like an upside down smiley but at least his determination had not failed.

Frederick, florid, fat and forty, the Director of Services, was proud of his achievements and this showed in his whole demeanour. He'd worked hard all of his life to reach that position. But now he was - like the lowliest of street cleaners - looking for a job. *Best make it a good meal, enjoy it. Get back a little of what was being wrenched away from me,* he thought as he chose paté and Beef Wellington, substantial, like him.

The only lady present, Isabel, the Head of Administrative Services, was a matronly, bustling and cheerful lady. She considered deeply and decided on just orange juice. *It has to be really fresh. That lamb shank sounds delicious in that red wine and rosemary sauce. Now I'll have to cut down on potatoes for the next week, but who cares? I won't be paying tonight.*

Paul collected the orders carefully. He knew his tip depended on getting this exactly right, after all. He moved gracefully to the kitchen with the order and returned immediately to ask what drinks were required. This was easy: 'One bottle of Chardonnay and two of Chilean Shiraz,' said the chairman.

Paul uncorked the bottles and poured wine according to individual choices. Then he stood back, pad in hand, and waited.

Tom, the Chair (as he preferred to be called), started the conversation. He pushed his spectacles back up his nose for the umpteenth time. He'd lost a lot of weight this last year but that is to be expected when the Government decide on a Unitarian Authority. The little man could not win and this little man was looking forward to his retirement. Already past his sixty fifth year, there was no point in his looking for re-election. Besides, his wife Martha had insisted that she'd had enough of following him around like Mary's little lamb to all sorts of stupid functions that she truly did not enjoy.

Now his words did not betray his thoughts as he asked, 'Well, what are everyone's plans?'

David was first to respond, 'Well, I'm on the dole, I suppose, for the first time in my life. No need for two Directors and the Controller's job has already gone to Jack, the incumbent. No I'll just have to look to private industry I suppose, not that there's much of it about these days.' He sat back, breathless and gloomy.

Isabel spoke apologetically, 'Of course I'm staying, they still need someone to control the local administration.' She paused. 'I suppose being an officer rather than a director has its advantages?'

David glowered darkly at her, he remembered having gloated to Isabel when he'd originally been given the Director's post.

Derek interjected. 'Me? I tried for the new Head of Council's Personal Assistant's job at Durham, but apparently got pipped at the post by some hot-shot straight out of University. I hope they don't expect me to show him the ropes as I just will not do it.' His tone was vitriolic. 'At least I've got this job with Cleveland Council, not a P.A. but it'll do till I find better.'

'At least,' said Tom, frowning, 'you'll be working and not forced into retirement like me.'

At this point Paul served each of them with their starters. They sat there eating them in solemn silence.

Alan broke the silence. 'Well, I suppose I'll be the happy medium as I'm going into semi retirement - private accountancy, you know? I've a few friends still in business, so I suppose I'm fortunate.'

'You certainly are,' said David. 'Wish there was some way we could come out of this in such a winning position.'

'Thinking about it, we might not take information with us. But what we could do is *hide* some information,' said Stephen quietly.

Paul smiled as he cleared away the empty plates.

'Just what do you mean by that?' asked David.

'I don't want to be involved with anything like that,' said Isabel. 'I think I'll just go and powder my nose.' She picked up her bag, stood up and made for the door marked *Ladies*.

Watching her weave her way past the tables Paul realised that he should make sure her meal came last. So he brought in the T-bone steak and the Salmon first, followed quickly by the tureens of vegetables and the Chicken and Beef Wellington.

While Isabel was powdering her nose, the men discussed strategies of damage, each deciding how to go about his own form of attack with the least effort. Paul moved quietly around the table, placing plates before the customers, ending with Isabel's lamb as he saw her returning, and bringing an extra tureen of steaming, fragrant vegetables.

Conversation changed on Isabel's return and family and friends became the topic of conversation. Tom's plan to take Martha on holiday to Spain was greeted with smiles. Isabel spoke of her daughter's wedding and her son getting a place at Exeter University. Stephen told how his plans to ask his girl to marry him had been spoiled by this situation. David spoke of his plan to start gardening in earnest. 'Always wanted to grow my own vegetables,' he said, stabbing at the last roast potato with unexpected dexterity.

Paul approached the table again, notepad in hand. 'Would anyone like to order dessert?' A smile hovered around his mouth as he wrote down their wishes.

- *Chair, Treacle Sponge.*

- *Alan, Peach Melba.*

- *Isabel, (just fruit, no cream).*

- *David, Banana Split.*

- *Derek, Cointreau Bombe.*

'How predictable,' thought Paul. He went away to order, returning at length with each item perfectly presented.

The guests ate their various desserts with relish and ordered coffees alongside five-star brandies for everyone.

'It's a shame really,' said Dennis, 'that they stopped smoking in restaurants or we could have ordered cigars too.' He watched Isabel's nose wrinkle at the thought and smiled.

When the bill was presented Dennis asked Paul to see the manager, alluding to the fact that this was their last meal as Council representatives. Paul complied happily and went away to get the manager, leaving him to complete the bill process.

He waited at the desk, continuing to make notes in his second notebook. When the manager returned to the till he took a twenty pound note from his pocket and pressed it into Paul's hand. 'This is to thank you Paul, for all your good service here, working hard to pay way through University.'

'I've enjoyed the work here sir.' He paused. 'It's surprising what helpful information you can pick up as a waiter.' Smiling, he followed his customers out to the car park and each thanked him for his good service.

'By the way Paul,' said Dennis as he climbed into his chauffeur-driven car, 'I understand you're leaving tonight.'

'Yes sir,' smiled Paul. 'I have this new job to start on Monday,' he said as he quietly closed the door of the car.

'And what's that, young man?'

'Well sir, I'm to be the new P.A. to the new Authority's Head of Council.'

# Hooked

## Mary N. Bell

It was one of my habits on a sunny afternoon, after I'd collected my prescription, to sit on the seats opposite Ferry's Pharmacy, and watch the world go by. One day a weary looking woman with red hair followed me out of the chemist's and came to sit beside me.

She offered me a sweet from a packet and started to talk. 'All these drugs have ruined countless lives, haven't they? You were in there, saw them swig down the Methadone. Restless till they get a fix, then straight down to the phone on the corner to ring the drug dealer. Methadone's just another fix, supposed to keep them under control. If you come and watch at the weekend when they get a dose in a bottle to tide them over till Monday, they swig the whole lot down, throw the bottle in the gutter, and then off to the phone. They wake in the night thinking about the next fix, it's not a question of getting up in the morning to enjoy the day – just the next fix. You want to know how they start. When they are out socialising they start off with E - ecstasy. With this they go into different realms – see bonny colours and things like that. They try Magic Mushrooms – hallucinating, not a big enough kick. Marijuana, anything to get a better or higher kick. Then they talk about dope, try it, use it. That would be alright to them, they would put it in a cigarette, sprinkle it in – smoke it. A better experience, slowly they are getting hooked. Then they smoke other stuff – next cocaine, put it in tinfoil and sniff it. They are hooked. They are addicted, known as druggies.

My friend's spoons began to go missing, 'Where are they?' she asked. She had three left out of twelve. Someone, I won't mention names, was using it by heating heroin up in the spoon and then injecting it. A bigger hit this – wow – this is great, gives them clarity of mind – you know how we all would search for inner peace. I'm happy, they think. I'm settled. That's great – but when they come down they look for more.

D-tox 5. Have you heard of it? £3000 it costs the National Health, per person, but that is trivial considering what it costs for Methadone, then living allowances, so this is cheaper than long-term treatment.

D- tox 5 gets its name because when they go to the clinic which is at Harrogate, they have to go five days without heroin, supplemented, that is not so bad as being 'cut dead' from drugs. Then you would be ill. They ask what you have been taking and you have to be perfectly truthful, they have to know this before starting treatment. From that info they find something suitable to sedate you with without killing you because with the stuff you have been taking it's a fine line between whether you end up alive or dead. Just needs the wrong dosage and you will be dead. The doctor is perfectly honest about this.

This young man I am talking about told the doctor and it was shocking to think the amount of tolerance he had built up. When they first start to go on drugs they get the wow factor, after that they need a little more and more so they get a high.

He was taking per day – ten blues – i.e. Diazepam 10 mgms. These are sleeping tablets you would normally take at night, one only. He was taking ten, swilled down with about four bottles of strong cider, 2 litre bottles and 3 bags of heroin or cocaine a day! White powder. The doctor said, 'How you aren't dead I don't know.' He had a really high tolerance. He went on to D-tox with Largactil which was a way of calming his mind down. After 5 days he went home, they gave him a blocker, Nantroxil. As soon as he took that he said it was as though he was being burnt throughout his body. He was absolutely freezing and violently sick and had severe diarrhoea. A living hell. So painful if he took any drug he would vomit or have diarrhoea. That lasted three months, then he began sneaking back to drugs.

The addicts should get their Methadone elsewhere, not at the local pharmacy as they can put the ordinary folk off from going there, then they too would have some privacy. Don't forget, they are human too!

There have been stabbings caused by drugs as they don't know what they are doing, they seem to have a change of personality. A woman I know has a job as part-time post woman to feed her son's habit. Goes out in all weathers, daren't refuse him money or else. It pulls at your heartstrings, it is frightening.

Sitting here I saw an old lady mugged after she had drawn her pension. Hangings, overdoses - accidental or otherwise - kill some.

Evil that's what I think – it is not just the drugs it is the company they keep. The power that is supplying is pure evil – there is evil behind it.

Alcohol can be bad but with drugs they are not even themselves, they are a nasty piece of work. They think they are invincible. See him walking down the street, think that is an ordinary cigarette he is smoking? No, that is spliff, can tell by the size. Lads here, and girls and women walk about like zombies, living dead. Don't wash – don't clean their teeth, then loose their teeth due to drugs, then ask at the chemists for sugar-free methadone. Drugs are killing them and they ask for sugar-free methadone!

Youngsters from good families are often targeted because they have the money. Problems in society are nearly all associated with drugs. Church-goers and do-gooders do not see the real world. It is here all the time. It is a big problem not to be taken lightly.

These addicts are human – half of them are very nice but with this stuff in them they turn into monsters. The young man I was talking about is one of those you have just seen get his Methadone and straight to the phone. A lovely child, my boy, he was always top of the class. We were so proud of him.'

She picked up the empty Post Office delivery bag and she was gone.

*When the pit closed Easington and Horden changed. The drug culture arrived. It affected all the communities. Families learned about drugs for the first time and people spoke to me about their concerns. They became afraid to go out at night and fearful for the destruction of their community.*

# Easington

## Susan Robinson

Lost shape
Lost stature and vigour
Torn down
Bit by bit
Bulldozed into scrap
And driven to oblivion
The pit
Struck down
With the cancer
Of growing old
And as my father wasted
So did the site
That held the memory of life
In teaming coal trucks
No longer needed.

Blown up, decimated
We watched, unable
To change
This course of action
We saw it fall
A crash to earth
That shook the ground
We stood on
Wiped out
Obliterated
Buried beneath clay
A pit cage – its husk
A monument
Like a tombstone
On his grave.

*The demolition of the pit became associated in my mind with my father's illness and remains so to this day.*
*I can't think of one without the other.*

# Each Tree

## Mavis Farrell

Each tree is the soul of a man
Who lost his life
For the price of coal
In the Duckbills seam
In the firedamp hole
Each tree is the soul of a man

Each tree is the soul of a man
A father, a son
A husband, or brother
A neighbour and friend
Or somebody's lover
Each tree is the soul of a man

Remember these men as you walk
Through the trees
Leaves filter the sunlight
The whispering breeze
Is telling their story
For those who can hear
Each tree is the soul of a man.

# What's In a Name?

## Ann Peel

Charlie quickly donned his casual jacket and jeans. He was going to collect Davy and together they would get the bus to Hartlepool. New suits were all they needed now. On the way up Anthony Street, Charlie reflected on the kind of suit he should get, maybe he would leave the choice to Davy. He had a better idea of what people liked.

At his knock, Davy's Mam opened the door wide. 'Come in son,' she said. 'Our David's nearly ready. Won't be long.'

Charlie sat down in the nearest armchair, tapping his steepled fingers together.

'Practising your fingering lad?' asked Mrs Crockatt.

'Gotta keep them supple, Mrs C. Accordion is a tricky instrument you know.'

'You've got a real gift pet, I love hearing you play, especially *Happy Wanderer*. Now that's really my favourite.'

'Anyone can tell that,' he grinned. 'The the way you always lead the singing!'

Davy bounced into the room. 'Ready for off Charlie? Let's hit Burtons and sort out their smartest!'

'Okay Davy. Thanks for the chat Mrs C,' Charlie said over his shoulder, following Davy out of the front door, trying desperately to keep up with Davy's long strides and failing miserably. Out of breath, he followed doggedly, listening to his friend's view on colour and cut, material and buttons - all Davy's speciality.

All Charlie could do was smile. Playing the accordion was his only talent and everyone seemed to think he did it well - so much so that the planned suits were for Davy and himself to wear at their latest engagement next Saturday, playing for the first Over Sixties Club in Peterlee. Should be easy, he thought. The Oldies loved the old songs and he knew most of them off by heart. He just needed a few sheets of music and he already had them at home in the accordion case. With Davy leading the sing-a-long, they should have a great time with the old folks and the extra money would certainly come in handy.

At last the Hartlepool bus arrived and the journey passed very quickly for the two boys. Half an hour isn't long when you have so much to discuss. They decided not to wear Teddy Boy suits, because the oldies don't like Teddy Boys do they? They would wear drainpipe trousers though, because they were neater, less trouble than Oxford bags. No creases.

'OK then,' said Davy, 'Black trousers and we'll check colours for jackets when we get there eh?'

They decided on the Co-op tailors because Charlie's boss had said that Mr Locke was a good guy and would be sure to get their suits back for next Saturday morning. Straight down Church Street to the imposing and ornate Co-op building. The Tailoring Department was easy to find - first right at the main entrance. Charlie supposed the dapper man with the fine moustache was Mr Locke and they approached him, smiling amicably.

'What can I do for you gentlemen?' smiled Mr Locke.

'Well, what we want is a pair of black drainpipes each,' said Davy. 'And would you be able to make us a couple of matching jackets for next Saturday?'

'Depends on the jackets really. What are they for?'

When the lads explained he smiled and said, 'I remember how much fun it was, entertaining. You're certainly right to think hard about colours.'

'You an entertainer?' asked Charlie.

'Me? I was first violin on the Queen Mary for a few years.' The boys' faces showed how impressed they were. Then he showed them saxe-blue, mustard and lovat green serge. The latter won. Mr Locke took out his order book and wrote down their measurements. 'Should be ready in good time gentlemen, now all we need is your store club numbers.'

'What's that?' they asked in unison.

'Not members? OK. Just your names and a deposit will do and the balance when you collect them.'

'That's fine,'said Charlie. 'We'll take the trousers now.'

Money paid, Mr Locke said, 'That's fine gentlemen and now can I have your names please?'

'Well,' said Davey, 'I'm Davy Crockatt and this is my friend Charlie, his surname is Chaplin.'

'How dare you waste my time you, you hooligans!' shouted the tailor.

'But it's true,' pleaded Charlie.

'You can't fool me,' frowned the angry man. 'If you are serious, you won't mind paying up front will you?'

'Suppose not,' said Davy.

'But it means no nights out at all this week,' said Charlie ruefully.'Still it will be worth it.'

Emptying their wallets and pockets they found just enough to cover the cost of their suits and the fare home. Feeling very disgruntled they made their way home without even their pint at the Grand.

Davy's Mam laughed and laughed. She said that she'd wondered how long it would take for their names to get them into trouble. They had already avoided using them on stage, choosing Trendy Tempos instead. How many times had she told them to carry their birth certificates?

Saturday morning found them back at the Hartlepool Co-op Tailors, with Mr Locke still looking suspicious, waiting to fit their perfect jackets. They were thrilled at the finished effect. They looked cool, not at all stuffy as they had suspected. Mr Locke complimented them on a good choice and wished them well for their evening performance. 'I still can't understand why you played that stupid joke on me last week. It quite upset me you know,' he said.

'Ah yes that reminds me, I brought this to show you,' said Charlie.

'Me too,' said Davy.

They laughed loudly at the expression on the tailor's face as he read their birth certificates. 'Well lads,' he said with a rueful smile. 'With names like those you'll get special treatment here in future to make up for me spoiling your week.'

That night the audience, which included Mr. and Mrs. Locke, enjoyed the entertainment. The Trendy Tempos glowed in the applause and grinned at Mr. Locke, who winked and gave a thumbs up.

These boys may not be as famous as their namesakes but they certainly were fun.

# Idle Hands

## Agnes Frain

Amy's voice was strident. 'What do you mean, you've applied for a job? Good grief, Mam, you're fifty four! When was the last time you worked in the big bad world?'

I stared at the wall as she continued her rant. One of the pictures was crooked. Quietly I put the receiver onto the tabletop and stretched over. Picture now straight, I bent my ear to the phone, she was still on high doh. I recalled past times when she'd bullied and cajoled her brothers and her Dad till they'd bent to her wishes. Now she used her wiles on her laid-back hubby. He was putty, putty that she shaped and remade at her whim.

She used these pre-arranged phone calls from her distant home to boss me about. I'd learned to ignore her sententious tone and her false promises to visit soon.

I picked up the phone and sat on the stairs, smiling at her protests for once. I certainly had her rattled. She was astounded at the news that her mam dared to venture into the world of employment.

'Mam, are you there?'

'Yes I'm here and that's the trouble, Amy. I'm always here, I need to get out. You obviously have no idea how much I miss your Dad. I'm lonely and time really drags. Just think. I spend my days rearranging the tins so all of the labels face the same way, then I move them into alphabetical order. Or I go into the bathroom and line up my soap and things into a nice pattern, then fold the towels perfect. Now I'm meddling with the book shelves, It's got to stop, Amy. I need a job.'

Silence.

Then I played my trump card. I knew her mind would be busy; she would be desperate to justify her infrequent visits. 'I have an interview lined up, and no, I won't tell you where. You'll find out soon enough if I'm successful.' I smiled as I replaced the receiver; no doubt her brothers' phones would be worked to death the rest of the afternoon. That thought made me smile. They would enjoy my triumph over their bossy sister. Their cry would be, 'Ignore her, Mam. Amy needs a drum to beat or she's not happy.'

I put up my hair in a loose knot and I ventured outside. My new boots clipped on the frost covered pavement as I walked down Cotsford Lane. I mused over the call and the fact that I'd not mentioned the anti-depressants my doctor had prescribed. I had forced myself to swallow these hateful things but now I yearned for work, to feel an uplift of spirits without their false high. Wherever I went I felt excluded, alone, an outsider. I craved to be needed again.

The low winter sun was just skimming the horizon as I neared my destination. Finally I walked under the old railway bridge on the road that led down to the beach. I glanced down at my hands as they rested on top of the wooden gate. These hands surely weren't my hands. They were short and stubby. Prominent veins jostled for space between multiple age spots. I dug my ragged nails into the wood and pulled at loose paint as I shed a tear. These same hands had cradled my babies; these hands had been my tools, they'd tended and soothed caressed and comforted. Adam's last action before he slipped away was to raise them to his lips and gently kiss my palms.

And now these treacherous hands wouldn't undo the catch, wouldn't let me force my body to follow them up the well-worn path to my destination. I shuddered; fear of failure and rejection totally halted my progress.

Voices! I turned from the gate. Two men, warmly clad in heavy waterproofs, rushed past, their boots loud on the beach road. Fishing gear hung around their bodies, they hurried like prisoners released from dark confinement towards the expansive shoreline of blackened sand.

The sea beckoned. With weakened legs, I followed the men. After all I needed time to rethink my actions.

Perched on a moss-covered boulder, I pulled my knitted scarf tight around the lower half of my face. Frost glittered on the rocks. The breeze carried the smell of seaweed and brine as one of the fishermen walked along the beach; he was busy gathering driftwood. Is this how men foraged long ago? This one dumped the wood near his fishing line, then out of one of his many pockets he brought some firelighters. Soon flames danced and other fishermen drew near. They huddled around the fire, comrades in adversity.

Wading birds caught my attention; they burrowed with their long beaks among the scattered pebbles, then stretched their necks as they gulped down sand worms. Sea gulls swooped low then shrieked in alarm as the flames spluttered and sent sparks into the cold air.

Pulling my thick coat closer, I scanned the horizon.

Small boats bobbed in the far distance. The grey surface of the sea looked cold and sinister, hiding its secrets. It struck me that, like the sea, I too hid my secrets below the surface, maintained to keep my sense of normality intact. How could I explain to anyone the thrill of waking each day aware of Adam, of his breathe as it stirred my hair. Then of the realisation that it was a dream crashed in on me. I was still in the reality of Hell. New every single day. Hell. It can't go on, I have to find a reason to want to get out of bed.

Now, today, filled with new vigour and energy after my rest, I rose, brushed down my coat and shook out stray sand, then retraced my steps back to the field gate, set between heavy posts. Now, decision made and doubt cast out, I leaned over to lift up the rusty catch.

My throat betrayed me as it started to tighten like a piece of stretched leather; my air passage narrowed. Then my chest heaved as my heart raced. It battered against my rib cage, callous and cruel. It galloped faster: cold sweat gathered on my brow as I gasped and struggled. I fought for air and my hands shook violently as I tried to loosen my scarf.

Not now, please, not now! With a great effort, I dragged my paper bag from my coat pocket and tried to blow. Again and again, desperate and alone, I tried to regain control. Blow, relax, blow, breathe. Then, after what seemed an eternity, my heart rate slowed.

Slumped against the gate, exhausted and wet with sweat and fear, I sank to my knees and rested my heavy head on the wooden gate. It was months since my last attack. Was this it? Was I beaten before I had a chance to prove my worth? My mind whirled like a rat on a wheel.

The low winter sun rose above the horizon and lit up the field. With heavy eyes, I looked towards the bungalow. It looked serene, bathed in the slanting light of the sun; smoke drifted from its steel chimney pot.

My strength began to return. Now was the time to make a choice, should I step out into the unknown or slink home and barricade my door? My legs trembled as I forced them to stand straight. Now the hands that reached to open the gate were stronger hands and it was time they earned their keep. I checked my hair, gave my boots a wipe on the thick frost-covered grass, and I was ready.

Horses snickered, then two beauties approached, hot breath blew from their nostrils as they waved their tails and lifted their delicate hoofs. I waited till they'd finished smelling me, then stroked and patted their out-stretched heads. Muscles undulated at my touch. They nudged and prodded me as I negotiated the path to the corner of the field where the wooden bungalow perched. Large beech trees stripped of their leaves made an arch as if they embraced and protected this small basic dwelling.

Clucking noises mixed with indignant squawks invaded my ears, and I saw reddish brown feathers float over the fence. A dog barked and a low melodic voice boomed. Was that the noise of snuffling pigs? My spirits soared. I could feel a smile as it stretched my lips, this was wonderful. This was my job, this I could do.

I remembered now my kindly grandparents and summers spent squashed into their tiny cottage. There too was the busy noise of hens as they scratched and fought in the small rented field adjoining the cottage. The smell of fresh cut grass and the rank odour of the muckheap - all were part of the magic spell cast on an imaginative child.

The breeze ruffled a few of my stray hairs, making me think of the gentle kisses Adam used to steal. Now I felt he gave me his blessing; I pushed open the bungalow gate.

Dozens of hens pecked and swerved as they ducked their heads to gobble at fresh green cabbage. They preened and swayed as agile as ballet dancers. And then I saw this giant, throwing this treat to the large hen. He was a vision of red: his shirt, freckled face and a shock of ginger hair clashed. He clucked and crooned, his face alight as he watched their antics. His thick corduroy trousers were double-secured with a belt and his tartan braces stretched over his plump stomach. With a wave of his hand, he invited me forward and strode towards an outside water pump. Water gurgled and splashed into a dented kettle.

Two snouts appeared over the top of a cement sty and the broad-backed white pigs squealed in outrage at being disturbed. The giant scratched their backs with a stick and they almost smiled. Embarrassed and unsure of what was expected I stood my ground as he continued with his chores. I edged closer as I tried to explain I was here about the advertised job for part-time help. The clamour of the hens and pigs drowned out my voice.

Why was I not afraid of this larger-than-life man? The noise of the animals as they continued their demand for food rose to a crescendo. Any cries of distress would go unheard and we were out of sight of any passer-by. Instead, I was relaxed and content. As a kaleidoscope of memories flashed, I almost shouted with pleasure. The giant turned and smiled, the kettle dangled from his hand, his red hair crackled in the winter sun and then he was illuminated with light....

*My grandmother was born in Norfolk and lived there in a farm cottage until she was twelve. Her parents, desperate for bigger wages to feed a growing family, moved to the North East to work in the newly-opened coal mines. Later in her life she was widowed and married my Grandad Logan, as we called him. He had a small-holding near Horden Beach and my Grandmother thrived there, saying she had at last returned to her roots.*

# The Man With Checky Socks

## Susan Robinson

That '*Who Do You Think You Are*' programme on the tele has a lot to answer for. It got me interested in finding my roots. Roots? Coal seams more like, seeing as I'm a colliery lass through and through. I imagine my family tree's roots stretch right down into the lower main, pushing up miner after miner along the way.

Start with your granny, they said on the programme. But there's the problem – my nan has Alzheimer's and doesn't remember - although she remembers she likes a tot of brandy or two.

She lives in Birchwood Court up the street; in that part of Easington Colliery that thinks it's in Easington Village. It's lovely in there - posh and all - but I'm not putting my name down, ever. Although it's true that the residents certainly have everything they need - while they wait to pop their clogs. *Devices for this, monitors for that, chair exercise and bingo.* What more could a person want amid the smothering smell of talcum powder and yesterday's dinner?

So I ask my mother about her dad, who she never talks about.

'I never knew him,' she says.

'Aren't you curious?' I ask.

'Well, me mam used to tell me fairy stories about him when I was little,' she says. 'Mam used to say 'The *Prince* This, The *Duke* That'. I got sick of the same old tales, so I stopped asking. I don't think your nan knew *who* he was. She was always romancing. You're just like her, you know - head in the clouds, making things up, telling stories. Sometimes, love, it's time to get real and accept things as they are. You'll just have to leave blank the entry on the family tree for your granddad.'

'Mam! Are you saying nan was a bit of a tart? Things didn't go on like that in her day, did they? She'd know who the father of her baby was, surely. I mean, unmarried mothers were unheard of, weren't they?'

'Why no, pet! Things were just the same, only more hushed up. She told folks that her 'husband' was away working on some lordship's estate. Can you believe it? She called herself Mrs and said she'd been married – quietly of course - in that tin chapel over in Horden. Clever, your nan, she knew nobody who went there. So no one could call her a liar.'

So, the next day off I trot to Birchwood Court – a fancy-pants name for a place that reminds me of Madame Tussaud's but with the waxworks in various stages of decay. To be honest it makes me shudder. Nan sits slumped asleep in a chair, only the chair wings keeping her upright. I touch her cheek. She feels like wax too. 'Nan. It's me!'

She opens her eyes abruptly, staring at me like she's spooked. Her cauliflower perm fluffs up around her head like shaving foam. 'Who is it?'

'It's me, nan. Annie, Betty's girl. I brought you a present.' I show her the top of the quarter bottle of brandy in my bag as I sit on the pittle-proof seat next to her.

Her eyes brighten. 'Give us a slurp, lass. Before them carers see.' She reaches out a twiggy arm, snatches, twists and swigs before I've had time to blink.

'Nan,' I say as she sits back again. 'I'm doing the family tree.'

'Well, you'll get nothing out of me.'

'Aw Nan, come on. Spill the beans. Tell me about my granddad?'

She leans back in the chair and takes another long swallow from the brandy bottle. It puts colour in her face and spangles her eyes. 'Eee! He was handsome, was Bert, regal like. Nothing like you or your mam. To be honest, you lot take after the common side of the family.'

'Aw thanks nan. Thought you couldn't remember any of this? Funny Alzheimer's *you've* got. Convenient memory lapse, more like.' She makes me laugh, she does. Couldn't fool a cuddy, that one. I nod my head at her, to jolly her along to say a bit more.

She purses her lips, bristling her chin hairs. She's got her dander up all right. There'll be no telling what she'll be like now. I pat her shoulder generously, to show I'm sorry.

'Don't you be forward with me, my girl. I'm saying nothing. I know the truth. It's best left alone.' She opens her handbag to stash the brandy away but I snaffle it and put it behind my back.

'Come on, nan. Please. Give me something to go on,' I plead. 'How did you meet this *la-di-da* bloke then? Tell me and I'll let you have the brandy back *and* get you another bottle.' I show her my best, simpering smile – the one she used to give in to when I was a bairn.

She hides her rubbery wrinkled face with veined hands as if she's crying but looks at me through her fingers; her nose with it's dusting of orange face powder like a large cheese wotsit poking out. If I laugh I've blown it. I nip my leg and frown. 'Poor Nan. Get it off your chest. You'll feel lots better, hinney pet.'

She belches - a side-stepping, boozy sigh belches in my direction. I must remember to bring her some mints next time. She hunches herself back in the chair, getting comfy. 'Well then, I met him on Hawthorn Beach. Me, I'm running along the shore, in my bare feet. I kind of do this little dance in the waves. Then I hear someone clapping and saying "Bravo". And it's him, this bloke. I'd never seen anyone like him before. Fine clothes and those checky socks, the ones posh blokes wear with them knicker things. He spoke gentle like, proper, with a little stammer. No pit slang for him. Oh! he was lovely. Nothing like the rough colliery lads I knew. Soft lips, soft hands. I tell you, he didn't stand a chance.' Her left eye twitches. I'm sure she's winking.

'What do you mean, nana?'

She goes red in the face. 'Let's have a drop more brandy, bonny lass. I'm out of puff.' She wipes her eyes with a screwed-up tissue and breathes wheezily, so I can hear just how much out of puff she has. She glugs almost half of what's left of the brandy, her lips sucked inside the bottle top, leaving a perfect round ring on her mouth when she's finished.

'Eee! I needed that. What was I saying? I forget. I'll just sip this last bit while I think; shame to waste it.' And the bottle is clamped to her lips again.

She starts to cough and splutter. Brandy spurts out all over. The bottle falls to the floor. Her chest heaves and she grabs at her throat. The noise she makes is fearsome, like a blocked Hoover hose. Her lips are blue. I wallop her back. All I feel are bones. It doesn't help.

After it's all over I go back to Birchwood Court to collect her things. In an old handbag is a newspaper cutting with a headline that reads *Royal Visit To Birchwood Towers.* Beside it is a picture of a man. At the bottom in nan's chicken scratch writing is one word –*Bert.*

I show this to mam. 'Isn't this ...... you know.... who?' I say.

This came out of my interest in family history and of finding instances where the father is cited as 'unknown'. My father-in-law also told a tale of the then Duke of York visiting Hawthorn Towers when it was a summer camp for boys, sometime in the 1930s.

# An Upside Down Story

## Joan Wright

There is a tale that can't be told
It hangs high from a tree
And there it shall forever dwell
The old man said to me.
What sort of tale, old man I said?
No-one will ever know
It shall remain a mystery
The gods have deemed it so.
Is the tree from which it hangs
Very far away?
Or is it nearby I said
Do tell me that, I pray.
You'll know Hawthorne Dene, he said
Indeed, I do declare
Search throughout it every day
And you'll not find it there.
I said a very fierce wind
Could blow it to the ground
In that case you'll agree
It surely would be found.
Or days and nights of heavy rain
Would wash the words away
Or a scorching summer sun
Would fade them soon, I'd say.
A tale suspended from a tree
Just beggars all belief
How can it hang there year by year
And never come to grief?
The secret is, it's upside down
At most unusual angles

The elements can't get to it
Whichever way it dangles.
Old man, I am intrigued said I
I'll search through snow and hail
I'll face all dangers far and wide
Until I find the tale.
Be on your way, young man he cried
You're gullible and daft
I've just told you a fairy tale
And how he laughed and laughed.
I said you've made a fool of one
Who lacks a sense of humour
His last words as I throttled him
Were oops I made a bloomer.
Then I'd a tale I could not tell
I dared not breathe a word
But guilt lay heavy on my heart
So I told my Granny's bird.
It stayed silent to the end
Then squawked I've got it Ned
And when Gran's friend, the bobby, called
Repeated all I said
Don't confide in parrots
They're smarter than you think
I've ten long years to muse on that
As I languish in the clink.

# Home

## Terry Dobson

Candles flickered as a gentle breeze came in through the open window. She sat at the mirror and carefully applied her makeup. She glanced at the clock. He was home tonight. Soon. He could even be on his way down Seaside Lane. She'd lit tea-lights and placed them on the stairs, a runway that lead straight to her.

She had butterflies in her stomach. Her mouth felt dry. Her heart pounded, excitement grew. It had been so long since they'd been together; that tearful farewell before his posting to Afghanistan. Tonight would be special.

She was full of nervous energy. Would he have changed? No. It had only been six months. He can't have changed that much. Another quick glance at the clock. Should she greet him at the top of the stairs? Or let him find her waiting?

She dressed carefully in the new silk lingerie she'd bought for the occasion, enjoying the sensual feeling as it caressed her skin. She saw the minute hand move from the corner of her eye. Where was he? Please let him be here soon.

Her foot trembled as nervousness and excitement went to war.

She jumped suddenly as she heard a key in the lock downstairs, and with a final flick of her lipstick she quickly crossed the room and posed seductively upon the bed, lit only by the flickering candles. There was a thump. Must be his bags as they hit the floor.

She tried unsuccessfully to take control of herself. Her breathing became faster and shallower with anticipation, and she felt herself become warmer. Her heart was beating so hard she thought he'd hear it. Her ears were alert for every sound. What was that? A footstep on the stair? Yes! There it was, the stair that always creaked. He was coming for her!

Suddenly the door flew open and there he was filling the doorway, his pilot's wings glinted in the candlelight. She sighed. Damn, he looked so good in his uniform.

'Hello,' she managed to get out the word.

With a broad smile he stepped quickly to her side. The moment she had waited for these long months finally arrived. She felt his warm breath on her skin as his lips drew closer, closer, and his strong arms wrapped themselves around her. His body was pressed against hers and she felt a warm shiver down her spine.

The kiss was hungry, passionate, filled with all the yearning of six months apart. They clung to each other for a while, and she could feel tears running down her cheeks. He placed his hands on her face and raised it so he could look into her eyes. With a smile, he wiped away the tears. She waited for what he would to say.

And now there it was, the soft voice she knew so well, as it whispered in her ear. 'Could you put the kettle on love? I'm parched.'

# Epitaph For The Hippodrome

Mary N. Bell

They're pulling the Hippodrome down
And what tales the bricks could tell
Of courting, dating and engagements
A few broken hearts as well.

Now it's to be a memory
Stored here within my brain
I'm beginning to like getting old
So that I can remember again.

Rain, wind, sun or snow
You'd see me set out from home
Three nights a week to see
The film on at the Hippodrome.

What pictures will you go to tonight
Was a phrase you heard on the street
I'll see you outside the Hippodrome
Friends and lovers would arrange to meet.

A queue to book your seat
Was a regular weekend scene
To make sure you didn't miss
The film on the silver screen.

Look who's coming in with who
Don't they make a handsome pair
See who that good looker's with
Whatever does he see in her

When the picture begins to reel
Every one is quiet and still
Any person who speaks out of turn
George gives a look 'fit to kill.'

For a couple of hours peace
If you left the kids at home
For one and six or less
You could relax in the Hippodrome.

I'm glad I was born when I was
Or I would never have known
That where houses will be in the future
Once stood our beloved Hippodrome.

# At Foxholes Point

## Susan Robinson

Sea-salt and bladder-wrack
Charge this electric atmosphere
Lit mauve with memory
Where a blue steel fence frames a haematite sea
And scrubbed land rises into cliffs
To fall achingly to the shore
Lonely gulls mock with haunted cry
While waves whisper against my ear
And trigger chords of sweet music
The Beach Boys sing
*Wouldn't it be nice?*
But the voice inside me cries
If only things could stay the same
Instead I know this is where he died
And every time now this thought
Stops and holds me
Captured in a breath
This feeling of regret
That I take with me when I go
Back home through Fox Holes Dene.

# The Path to Manhood

## Agnes Frain

The horse stubbornly picked her way to the open gate in the middle of the long colliery row leaving Billy, his scrawny arms aching, toting a heavy milk crate. Neck out-stretched, Dolly snuffled the offering of bread and jam held on the open palm of Mrs Plant.

'There my lovely,' she crooned as she stroked the preening horse. 'A warm stable is what you need, poor animal. Made to drag this heavy load.' She shot the young boy a sharp glance then slammed her gate.

The skinny teenager shook his head, his extremities were frozen; the cutting sleet was relentless. He tottered over the packed ice and snow as he strived to finish his round.

Children were making their way to school muffled up warmly against the raw morning. The sky looked heavy and oppressive: more snow was imminent. Billy picked up his speed. He heaved a sigh of relief when the last delivery was completed.

Now was the time to catch customers who still owed for deliveries. Billy heaved himself on to the stand in front of his cart and clicked his tongue. Dolly, aware she would be soon be out of the chill wind, set off at a brisk pace, her large feet sinking deep into the snow.

Billy hunched his shoulders and stamped his numb feet. His small thin frame ached, in spite of thick gloves and waterproofs the cold seeped into his bones. He coaxed Dolly up Cotsforth Lane. Snow began to fall, it whirled and settled into drifts.

Heads down, the pair plodded up the steep bank. Then Billy forced the protesting horse to halt. They were on the long road from the crossroads to the farm. Billy tied Dolly to a railing then made a detour into the housing estate to collect the last payments. He gave Dolly a pat and whispered a promise of a good ration of oats. Later, frustrated after fruitless banging on doors, the weary youngster retraced his steps. He sank into fresh snow almost up to his knees. Dolly! Where the hell was Dolly? This was where he'd left her. Trampled snow beside the fence plus a fresh pile of manure was all there was left of his elusive horse. He yelled and cursed and struggled up to the road. There she was, with her head up and mane flying, as she rushed to the farm for her feed and warm stable.

Billy cursed and shivered as he followed in her wake. He was close to tears but still marvelled at the horse's sudden turn of speed. Finally he found Dolly outside the bottle shed. He pushed past her, struggled to open the doors and unload the empty crates. 'Stand still,' he yelled as he unclipped the reins and harnesses. 'There! Now you lucky beggar, go and enjoy your feed and rest.'

Dolly entered the stables and greeted the other horses with a soft whinny. Eyes gleamed in the shadows as the farm cats gathered. Billy lifted the lid of the oat container then jumped to one side. Disturbed mice, with oats stuck to their whiskers, poured like a wave of water over the side. Cats screeched and slashed with extended fangs. Pandemonium reigned. Then with a lick of their mouths the satisfied cats stalked majestically out of the stable.

'Billy where are you?'

The boy ran out of the potato shed where he had been busy with the weights and   scales packing potatoes and bumped into Mr Fields. The farmer was an intimidating sight. He stood legs astride, his powerful body belied his age, and years of manual work had sculpted hard muscle. He looked down at the slight boy, then ordered him to take Patch, one of the milk-cart horses, to the blacksmith. 'One of his shoes is loose, hurry up! Be back before the second milking.'

Billy encouraged Patch up the ice-encrusted bank that led to Easington village. His feet tingled with the cold. This had been a rotten day. He'd had little opportunity to snatch hot drinks. The cold air that constantly circulated kept the potatoes at an even temperature but meant the dark shed had offered no warmth. Now the wind sliced through his waterproofs and the sky was dark.

'Hope he's not ready to shut his shop for your sake Patch, or he'll be in a paddy,' Billy whispered as they neared the forge.

Mr Stoker stood in the doorway, his powerful arms were bare; he dragged on a cigarette then snarled at the boy, 'Where've you been? Mr Field rang ages ago. I was ready to shut shop.'

The young boy's answer was rudely cut off as Mr Stoker ordered him to keep Patch steady. The blacksmith yanked off the old shoe as the piebald whinnied in fright.

But now Billy revelled in the heat, flames licked red and gold from the blackened forge. The tools gleamed in the low winter sun. Steam wafted from Billy's sodden clothes; surreptitiously he warmed his hands. Why, he wondered, was Mr Stoker always bad tempered? The skill of the blacksmith as he shaped and hammered a new shoe always filled Billy with admiration.

Sparks somersaulted and disappeared in the air; magic hands shaped and pounded; the clang of metal on metal was a sound centuries old. The blacksmith transformed lumps of iron skilfully; mistakes, impatiently dropped, landed with a clatter on to the hard packed ground. He made his finishing with a flourish: seven neat holes punched into the horseshoe.

Mr Stoker gestured to Billy to keep Patch steady as the shoe was hammered home using special studs to grip slippery cobbles. 'Right,' said the blacksmith, wiping his hot face with a filthy rag. 'Get cracking, lad, that's me finished for the day.' Leading Patch past the three huge byres, Billy's ears were assaulted by the sound of Ayrshire cows who bellowed and snuffled as they lined up, their distended udders heavy with the thick, creamy milk they produced in large quantities.

The byre-men threw open the milking sheds doors and the first hundred cows ambled in, then waited patiently to be attached to the machines. Soon the sound of liquid splashed and mingled with the clang of milk churns.

Billy led Patch into his stable and helped with the milk, rolling milk churns between the milking shed and the dairy. This hard work warmed young Billy. This was the time when every hand available was needed; an hour and a half passed before the last churn was emptied.  Then he helped to bed three hundred cows for the night.

At last Billy shouted goodnight to the dairymen then joined the other workers as they streamed up the bank to the Shoulder Of Mutton public house. Huddled around the fire there, they talked about their day. The youngster sat at ease as his companions quaffed their pints. He was accepted as their equal.

*My brother-in-law began working on a farm aged fourteen and a half. These events happened to him but not all on the same day.*

# Love Affair

## Mary N. Bell

I had this dream see
Turned to a nightmare,
I went to see you
You weren't there.

I stood at the place
Where we met often
The field was empty
Dust and bracken.

You broke my heart
Again and again
Killing and hurting
Like a wild hurricane.

It was a mad love affair
Between you and me
Since you've gone
I'm not sorry I'm free.

You were always there
I'd always had you
Love turned to hate
At the things you'd do.

Now you've gone
In my heart I'm glad
I sigh for the future
Hope it's not too bad.

I treasure your memory
That's all far behind
Redundant, renewed
I have peace of mind.

This affair of mine
Deep, dark, secret
Ended for good
Gone with... The Pit.

# Pink Suede Boots

## Mavis Farrell

Mavis Farrell

Ellie stands poised on the very edge of the pond, her small suede boots darkening from pink to red and from red to black as moisture from the rain-flattened grass soaks into them.

She is supposed to be safe at home in the terrace of old colliery houses arching like a dinosaur's back down the slope, towards the pond. A train flashes past along the embankment, too high up for Ellie to see but she knows it is the train, she knows the sound well.

Ellie had told a lie.

Her mother, coming home exhausted from night shift at the care home, had been met at the door by Mel dancing about from one foot to the other as she crammed on her crash helmet.

'Carol, Ellie's got belly ache so I didn't take her to school. She hasn't eaten. Gotta go...late for work already.' Then she was gone.

Ellie did have a sort of Daddy once. His face is a blur now but she remembers the smell of his sweat and the funny cigarettes. He has gone to Hartlepool to be somebody else's Daddy. Ellie doesn't miss him. Ellie loves Mel. She loves the big smiley mouth with the curled up corners and the spiky black hair which flattens under her crash helmet and needs to be re-spiked with gel.

Mel is the reason why Ellie had told the lie about the belly ache.

'Lesbo, lesbo, your mam's a lesbo,' the big girls in the school yard chanted every day. Ellie didn't know what they meant but she dreaded the sound of cruelty in their voices.

Carol checked Ellie's temperature, made her some toast and they snuggled under a blanket on the battered couch to watch CBeebies.

Carol didn't mean to sleep. She would carry the weight of self-blame for a very long time.

Ellie, bored with The Tombleyboos, got dressed in her new puffa jacket and pink suede boots and wandered down to the pond to look for newts.

The dark surface of the pond is littered with empty crisp packets and bobbing lager cans. A plastic Asda bag inflates like a sail where the light breeze catches it. An abandoned broken fishing net and a seaside pail lie scattered nearby. Ellie finds a stick and leans right over the pond to stir the murky water. Wet curly tendrils of dark hair cling around her elfin face in the autumn damp morning as her eyes scrunch up in concentration. Finding no newts in the stagnant mess, she looks around for something else to do.

An elderly couple and their overweight Jack Russell pass under the railway bridge onto the circular path, each foot is placed slowly with careful precision. Ellie follows. They turn right, along the edge of the railway towards Foxholes Dene. But Ellie goes the other way, towards the beach banks and the cliffs.

Droplets of last night's rain cascade from the red and yellow leaves as a blackbird abandons its perch and goes to feed on jewelled berries. Wet fallen leaves smell of autumn as the fat dog sniffs and worries about, longing for rabbits.

The old couple, Robert and Lydia, tired already, look in dismay at the filthy tramp who dares to sit on *their* seat at the mouth of Foxholes Dene. They need their usual half-way rest but the tramp smells very badly of filth, urine and alcohol. Exchanging glances which say all, they have no choice but to lean on the railings and look out over the grey sea towards Teesport and beyond. Their dog runs to greet the tramp but he swears in a rasping voice and frightens it away.

Ellie wipes her runny nose on the sleeve of her puffa as she kneels on the wet path watching snails with striped shells as they slither along on their journey through the remains of the fallen rain. Ellie wonders where they are going and how long it will take them and what they are thinking about as they go. The old couple trudge towards her, Robert limping and Lydia looking cross as she shouts for the fat dog who, as usual, takes no notice at all.

'What are you doing here on the beach banks by yourself?' Lydia asked Ellie.

Ellie doesn't answer, she doesn't exactly know what she is *doing here.*

'Where do you live?' asks Robert kindly.

'Number eleven Conway Street,' Ellie says.

'Does your mammy know you're here?'

Ellie looks back over her shoulder to the railway bridge where a young couple are just coming through. She nods in their direction.

'My mam doesn't mind,' she says.

Robert and Lydia continue on their way. On passing the young couple Lydia says, 'Don't you think your little girl is too far ahead? The cliffs are very dangerous.'

'We don't have a little girl. What's the problem?' Old Robert explains and the young ones, seeing how upset he is and how tired they both look, agree to find the little girl and take her home to Conway Street.

The young couple walk the whole of the circular path and, finding no one at all, hurry to Conway Street where they bang on the door, wake Carol and ask if she has lost a little girl.

The Police are everywhere. Houses are being searched, fields combed and the tracker dogs are sniffing frantically as they quarter the steep overgrown sides of Foxholes Dene. The golden hour has gone and the helicopter has been scrambled. It put-putters overhead, circling the beach banks, the cliffs and the sea as morning wears on and optimism wears out.

Lydia, hearing the helicopter, goes out into their garden. She watches as it circles. Fear explodes inside her as she clutches her chest and vomits on the cabbages. Robert, never any good in a crisis, fills the watering can and washes the vomit away before telephoning the police to tell them about the tramp.

The watery sun retreats as dark clouds stack up and the sky lowers itself onto the sea.

At seventeen minutes past four that afternoon the tracker dogs find a pair of small pink suede boots scattered well apart in the thick undergrowth of Foxholes Dene. When the tide retreats an hour later taking all hope with it, the helicopter crew locate a lifeless body rolling on the pebbles at the bottom of the cliffs.

The day drags itself to evening and then, in the click of a light switch, the day has gone. Carol and Mel live in a nightmare of fear and dread from which there is no waking. Mel goes into the kitchen to make coffee and hears the end of a message on the police woman's radio. *'.....the recovered body is that of a late to middle aged man, by his appearance probably a vagrant and as yet, unidentified.'*

'Mammy, Mel, I'm back. I've had such a very exciting day and I'm very sorry to have been out so long, I know I've been a bit naughty but I'm so hungry!'

Ellie stands inside the kitchen door, bits of bracken stuck in her tousled hair, face and clothes filthy but she is very much alive. On her feet she wears a pair of well-worn, brown leather T-bar sandals with crepe soles, a type not seen for fifty years or more.

'Ellie, are you alright? Where *have* you been? Thank God you're home.' Carol and Mel hug Ellie and smile through rivers of tears.

Much later when the police and the doctor have given up on their questions and examinations and Ellie had been bathed, fed and put to bed, Carol asks Ellie what had really happened.

'Tell me and Mel about your exciting day Ellie. We won't be a bit cross with you, honest we won't and we're dying to know.'

'Well, you fell asleep and I went to look for newts but there wasn't any so I went for a walk along the path       and there was this old man who said he would show me some rabbits in the woods but there wasn't any rabbits and he gave me some money and said my boots and leggings were wet so I should take them off. I took my boots off then I got a bit frightened of him. He smelled horrible.'

Carol gasps and shudders but Mel put her arms around them both and encourages Ellie to carry on with her story. They need to know.

'Just then two girls came. They shouted at him really loud and told him he was a dirty old man and he ran away towards the cliffs and we held hands and ran and ran the other way. I'm sorry mam I lost my new boots but Lilly gave me her sandals. She says her feet never feel the cold.'

'What happened next Ellie?' asks Mel.

'We went to Mr Henry's shop and bought some sweets with the smelly man's money and then we played all day in the Welfare Park.'

'Did you see the people looking for you?' asked Carol.

'Yes, but I was a bit scared to come home and Annie said no one can see me if I'm with them. It was really fun and I've had a lovely day.'

'Where do the girls live?' asked Mel.

'Their house has been knocked down. They used to live in Ayre Street, but now they live at the old school, not my school, you know the old one.

Carol and Mel look at each other and settle Ellie down to sleep, relieved that she is unharmed. But Carol wonders about *post traumatic stress syndrome.* Ellie seems unharmed and happy and there is no more talk of the events of that day and the mysterious girls in the months to come. It was as if the day had never been.

The old Infant school stands crumbling and gaunt with boarded up windows like blinded eyes. A thicket of shrubs and small trees thrust their way up through cracks in the playground, providing night perches for small birds and a hunting ground for feral cats.

On cold winter evenings darkness falls early and most people prefer to be at home with their curtains closed tight against the night and their central heating turned up high. The old couple are making their way home from the library. They are late because Lydia had felt quite poorly and Esther, the librarian, had kindly made them a cup of tea. They both turn at the shrill sound of childish laughter as they pass the schoolyard.

Robert wonders how the children managed to climb over the high iron railings with the spikes along the top. Lydia clutches her chest as the pain comes back. She holds out her hand to the little girl with the lovely face. And before the blackness comes she wonders why the child has bare feet on such a very cold night.

# Thoughts of the Sea

Terry Dobson

Sadness blue as summer sky
Gentle sigh of the sea
Soothes the grieving mind
And lets the thoughts flow free

Mood black as night-time shadow
Whispering of the sea
Exorcises the haunted mind
And lets the thoughts flow free

Anger red as fresh spilled blood
Cleansing waves of the sea
Calms the raging mind
And lets the thoughts flow free.

# Northern Shores

## Susan Robinson

Salt crusted clothes
Wind spiked hair
A purple lidded sky
Hangs over a monochrome sea
Waves thrash the shore
Then stroke it in apology
Bladder-wrack
Tells the thick and glossy weather
And I find sea-glass
To wind with silver wire.

This poem came to me walking on the beach past the Horse Back on a wild and wonderful day

# Queenie's Lament

## Agnes Frain

More rubbish! ooh me poor back!

Time I had one of those fancy net baskets over this letterbox, bloody landlord he knows I have a bad back, does he care? Does he heck.

Unfeeling beggar, living in his flash house in the lap of luxury. He's got a nerve, yaps and bullies at me. Me, a defenceless widow. Just because I'm a bit behind with the rent. Well, quite a lot behind, but so what? How can I afford it? I reckon it's that smug Gerry Crumlick that owes me money. He lets me live in squalor then he gets most of the rent from the social.

When you think of it he should *give* me this house. It's cramped, it's smelly. Who else wants this dump? I ask you. Time he pulled out a bit of cash; there must be moths breeding in his pockets or he has short arms because he never digs deep.

The rogue, he's forgotten I'm a widow.

Herby, ah my Herby! Now there *was* a man. A lazy beggar at times but a swift kick where it hurt used to send him double quick to work. Ah, they were happy days. How many years since my Herby died? Our Tot had just started school and he's what? Let me think - I know I sent him a fiver. Twenty one! That's right, twenty one.

He sent me a note from London last week, told me he'd been on the binge with his mates. Never thanked me for the fiver, though. The ungrateful sod. I scraped and scrimped for my kids, and then what happened? They all scarpered like ferrets up a drainpipe as soon as they left school. They made damned sure I didn't get a sniff of their money. After all my struggles! All I got was a glimpse of their backsides as they ran out the door.

Sixteen years without my Herby! Talk about being diddled. Cancer of the bone, no wonder with all these pesticides about. He breathed them in every day, didn't he?

That Crumlick used my Herby – all those sprays he was made to use; every bloody insect was hunted down and murdered. 'Just keep my properties' gardens tidy, Herby,' he would say. He made it sound so easy. No mention of *our* house. Oh no, what he meant was the *posh* houses in the village. The fuss he made about feeding and spraying. The property that twister owns, I bet he's a millionaire, that mean landlord of mine.

Dr Scope laughed, yes laughed, when he said if pesticides were the cause, half of England would have bone cancer. Well he would, he's a big pal of Prince Crumlick. They're all the same, thick as thieves, these rich men.

My man was as strong as an ox. I've seen him carry a deer home, just slung over his shoulders. The poor beast, dying it was, cruel to leave it in pain, got hit by a car. Herby was just coming out of the Dene after midnight one night. Anyway he tripped over the animal. My Herby soon put it out of its misery, poor dumb animal.

Yes, my hubby should have lived to a ripe old age.

Big deal! That twister Crumlick brags he's generous, letting me stay in this house. What was he going to do? Chuck out this poor defenceless widow with four kids? All those years paying a pension and what did I get, scraps, a pittance? Now he's after more rent. Well he can whistle for it, take me to court. They can't get blood out of a stone can they?

Where's me hanky? I feel quite upset.

If there's any bills among this lot they can get lost. By the time I buy a few fags and a couple of bottles of plonk what's left? A few measly quid. I have to eat, don't I? Or is that another rule, widows aren't allowed to eat. And if I go to the pub I have to buy a drink or I'll get me marching orders.

Mind you, there's plenty of fools who'd buy me a drink if their wives weren't around. Jealous they are, frightened of my charms. Who'd want to pinch one of that lot? The gormless idiots.

Now Ernie, he's more my style, a big man, if you follow my drift. Never comes near me in the pub. Ooh! Just the thought of his sly wink gives me goose pimples. Blimey, I thought we'd been scuppered last night, the times he accidentally brushed past me, I was all of a dither.

Where's me handbag? Where's that note? God what a scruffy mess! This needs digging out, but not now. I can't be bothered. Here it is.

*Tomorrow night my little princess, be ready.*

That's cheered me up, I'll put it next to me heart. Ooh! He's so romantic. That daft wife of his, thinks she's better than me. She's a skivvy for the posh crowd. Catch me doing that. I've enough to do. Well! When I feel like it. Keeps her money close does that one. Fancy, it comes to something when the man of the house - him suffering from a bad back - has to thump her to get money for a pint. Now me, he knows where he is with me, I give him plenty of loving.

Ah well. What's this about? Another electric bill, there's another set of robbers. I'll ask our Jack for a bit of cash. Surely he won't let his old mum sit in the dark. Come to think of it, *he's* never been near since Christmas Day.

That was a farce, him swanking down the lane in his new car. Gets to his house, what happens? Frosty face glares at me all afternoon. Well! The chicken was an old boiler. Bloody meat was like leather. I had to take me teeth out as they were killing me. Then *she* turns her nose up at me wine. I get what I can. *I* haven't got a man to keep me in luxuries. Our Jack drank plenty, and the kids. I saw them slurping it down in the kitchen. It's a good job I took three bottles. We had this great sing-song and could those kids dance! They loosened up a treat.

I thought Frosty Face was going to bust a gut when our Jack fell asleep. He snored like a pig and she and couldn't rouse him. Cost her a fortune that taxi. Did I ride home in style! Laugh? It made my day.

Funny, never seen hide not hair of him since that day, I'll just have to find some coppers and give him a call.

What time is it? Eleven o'clock! It's time for my medicine. Empty! I can't remember draining the bottle. Only Monday and my purse is full of fresh air, a couple of measly quid. Well, Queenie girl, get searching, pockets, chair, ashtray. Right! Another quid. That'll have to do. Might get me a bottle of plonk. Can't disappoint Ernie, can I?

What's this? Another letter stuck in the letter-box. My I'm popular today. The cheek! Will he ever stop picking on me? *Tidy the garden or you face eviction, this is your last warning.*

That's the last straw. Where's that photo of our Tommy? It comes to something when a decent woman is driven to threats. His wife will sort him out the lecherous beast.

Calm down, let him rant. Just a minute, I'll ring the Echo, that reporter the muck-raker, what's his name? Sam Sleaze, I'll get him to call. Hang on hang on. Stop, better not. The whole blooming village will be banging on my door, they'll tar and feather me if he starts prying into what goes on in this village.

Where's that fag gone? Don't tell me somebody nicked it from my bag. God what a mess! Flattened. It'll have to do. No wonder I drink. Just what have I done? Everybody hates me. OK I yell at kids when they trample my garden. As for gossiping, who doesn't? So I cadge! Well, give me some more money and I wouldn't have to. They make me sick, pretending I'm a bad smell. The drink keeps me sane and my fags - begrudged they are, begrudged. A hovel to live in, four selfish kids, no wonder I can't work. Stressed, that's what I am. Stressed!

Look at me hair it's falling out, what's Ernie going to think of his lovely?

Where's me coat? Let me get out of here. Would you look at that! Those cheeky kids, sitting on my bench. They might be little but they're monsters. Look at them giving me the finger.

I need a man in the house, a big man. That'll give me a bit of clout. What about when I'm old, who'll look after me? Will I be left to rot?

Right! Fags, wine and charm. I'll get Ernie to marry me if it kills me.

Where's me comb and lipstick? A bit of scent, pooh that stinks! Must be off. Look at your poor down-trodden face, smile, go on Queenie, smile! What's that stuck on me teeth? I'll give them a sluice. This is what I get for trying to please other people - walked on, trodden on, spat on. Time I had a bit of respect. Get your head up Queenie, don't be meek, fight for your man!

Where's me key? If I leave the door open those kids will get in here and pinch my treasures.

# The Striker

## Susan Robinson

William Pitman barricades himself in the polytunnel. He timbers up the doorway with anything he can lay his hands on. He throws potted-up seedlings to the ground in his haste to get at the shelving, to drag it over to block the entrance. Mad as hell, he stacks grow-bag upon grow-bag to add weight to his fortifications, not caring that tomato plants are crushed and months of careful nurturing are wiped out. He bangs his head with his hands in frustration at the news he doesn't believe he's just heard. Easington House, Mental Health Community Care Hostel is closing. Imminently. So William's gone on strike. They'll not get him out. He's not going to bloody Hartlepool. He doesn't care that they say it's nice there. He's lived in Easington all his bloody life, man. Friends are here, his gardening is here, his routine is here, all he knows is here.

He sits on the ground among the smashed-up plants and cries because he doesn't know what else to do. The tears irritate his stubbled jaw and he scrubs at his face trying to rid himself of the feeling. It's hopeless. It's just bloody hopeless. He's too old to move away. He'll be seventy six next birthday. He'll just stop here, in this poly-tunnel until he dies. Short of burning it down they'll not get him out. There's water, the remains of the cheese sandwiches he'd brought in yesterday, and the packet of digestive biscuits for his ten o'clock. It'll be all right. He's been through worse things than this.

William remembers the great strike of '84: the picketing, the hardship, the camaraderie. *United We Stand!* But this time he's on his own. Not even his missus is here now. She went and died and he couldn't cope. That's why he's here. Not because he's mental. He just gets confused sometimes and a bit anxious. Like now.

There's a tapping on the poly door, and a shadow grows big against its frame.

'Bill.'

'Who is it?'

'It's Daz. Daz Newcombe. You know. Your buddy.'

William blows his nose on a dirty hankie. 'You're not me buddy. I don't know you. Comin' in here. Think I'm your friend, you got another think comin. You're a bloody stranger to me. I don't like strangers.'

'Listen, Bill, I don't make no rules. They tell me I'm your buddy, and now they tell me to come and have a chat with you. Calm you down, like. I don't want no trouble, me. So I do as I'm told.'

'Me name's Mr. Pitman to you and I'm not talking to you. Bugger off.' William reaches for the stale sandwich. He's hungry. It must be dinner time, he can smell vegetables cooking. His stomach rumbles. It's beef stew today. One of his favourites. But he's made of strong stuff. He'll not give in.

The shadow looms closer and a finger, then an eyeball appears in a slit in the plastic.

William stabs the air twice with his finger. He's not talking to that bloody yobbo.

'Watcha been doing Mr Pitman? Kicking off and tearing the place up don't help. I should know. You gotta fit in, man. No dramas.' Daz has his face in the slit now.

William scowls. He looks around him. Leeks as thin as blades of grass, grown from special seed, lie broken and limp on the ground. His pride and joy.  His show leeks.

'Look what they made me do. The rotten buggers.' He tries to pick up the damaged plants. 'I cannot do it, man. All this bother's set me vibration white finger off.'

'Let me in, mate. I'll do it for you.'

'You? What're you after, like?'

'Look, I'll put my hands up. I've got to prove myself, close the case.  I got involvement with you, bruv. We're supposed to help each other in here. It's no problem, mate.'

'I don't trust you. You look like one of them hoodies off the street corner. Do you know what to do, even?' William rubs his knobbled fingers on his corduroy trousers. The pain's bad the day.

'You can show us what to do. It can't be too hard. Who showed you, like?'

'Me da.'

'I ain't got no da.'

'No da?'

'That's right, mate. It's a shit world, innit?'

William takes a knife out of his pocket. 'Here, hold on a minute.'

'Watcha doin with that, mister?' Daz's shadow fades from the poly-tunnel. 'I don't want no trouble, bruv.'

William sticks his head through the polythene, making sure the lad's on his own, then he cuts through the plastic, making the slit big enough to squeeze through. 'Howay in, then. Behave yourself, mind. I was in the T.A. you know. I can take care of meself.'

'No probs, Mr Pitman.' Daz sticks out his hand. 'It's a deal, then?'

'I don't know about that, kidder. Let's see you sort these leeks. Then I might shake your hand.' William shows Daz how to save what they can of the damaged plants, setting and firming them in fresh compost. 'Where you from, then?' William offers Daz a black bullet, one of two he's found in his other pocket.

'Down South. But me mother lives in Horden.'

'So why don't you go and live with her?'

'She'll not have us. Said once I got out of Durham nick I was on my own. I'm getting a house in some estate called Wembley next week.  Funny that, thought the only Wembley was down where I'm from. Got any more of those kets? I'm starving, we've missed the grub.'

'What you in for?'

'Dealing. I was set up, though.' Daz texts on his phone, his thumb flying over the keys. 'Mistaken identity, Mr Pitman. It wasn't me, honest. I'm telling you the truth.'

'Do you mean drugs? You don't do them things, do you?

'No, not me. Not real drugs, anyways. I'm no crackhead.'

The two of them restore a sort of order to the polytunnel. It takes some time. The battered tomato plants stand humped over in their grow-bags on the ground. The shelving is back in its place and seedlings stagger in different directions in their pots, as if hit by a strong wind.

Someone in the garden outside whispers. 'Daz..... Daz, mate!'

Daz disappears through the slit in the plastic and then reappears carrying a couple of carrier bags.

'Here you are Mr Pitman. Supper.'  He hands William a can of Carling and a polystyrene food box. Inside is a kebab from *Geordie's*.

William's famished. The cheese sandwich was a long time ago. 'Champion,' he says. 'You're a canny lad. Daz – what's that short for, then?'

'Darren.'

Bits of salad and garlic sauce decorate William's chin. 'I don't usually eat foreign muck like this. But it's not bad, I'll give you that.' He rummages around in the food tray making sure there's nothing left. He stuffs the last piece of pitta in his mouth before taking a long pull on the beer. 'How is it you're getting a house Darren? Up Wembley an' all? Why, a man had to work thirteen years at the pit before he got a house there, and only if he was *in the know*.'

'Cos I'm classed as homeless,' says Daz.

'I'm homeless and all. But I'm not going to bloody Hartlepool.'

'You can come with me, if you like, straight up. You can show us things. You know, like a dad.' Daz rolls a couple of smokes. He hands one to William. 'A spliff a day keeps the doctor away, Mr Pitman,' he says with a grin.

'You can call me Bill, son.'  William holds out his hand for Daz to shake.

# To Easington

## Avril Joy

We drive east across a skim of snow
in the spell of sunrise arriving
at a place where the North Sea swells the
dip in the bank and fills the sky with ink.
A place that does not boast instead plants
trees in quiet avenues of unadorned regret,
on snow, on grass, on ashes lie beneath
a seam of memory diamond hard coal
black and cobbled drawn across
uncertain paper - scholarships won
postings abroad, graduations hard forged,
divorce unheard of then when innocence
saw cars stood signalling the sibling's birth
daughters scooped up onto horse's back
black books, black looks and accusations
unmasked in this place that does not suffer
affectation - no bankers, fat cats or
soft southerners here bar me of course
all hewers impervious to attack from
the elements and the high seat of power
from the faithless measure of science
and the parade of all fate's armies,
it endures as sea as coal as memory,
as we drive homeward west.

# Biographies

## Easington Writers

**Mary Nightingale Bell** was born and bred in Easington Colliery. She was educated at Easington Colliery Infant and Junior schools, then Seaham Harbour Grammar School. A retired nurse, she writes stories and poems of pit life, many of which have been published. Mary is the founder member of Easington Writers

**Terry Dobson** grew up in Horden and later moved to Blackhall Colliery via Peterlee. A 44 year old pagan, slowly turning Goth in his mid-life crisis, he has had two short stories published and is currently working on a supernatural thriller. Terry has an eighteen year old autistic son, who is a published poet.

**Mavis Farrell** - is a new writer. Born in Lancashire, she has lived in Easington for forty two years. In former lives she was a tracer in a drawing office, a herdswoman, a shop assistant, a waitress and a bar person. She recently retired from a career as a community midwife and now writes and paints.

**Agnes Frain** - was born in Horden. She is married with three children and four grandchildren. In her forties she successfully took her O and A Level exams. Since retiring from a nursing career she has finally found inspiration to write short stories and believes that her 'locked imagination has been freed, thanks to her writing group.'

**David Lee** – David was born in Horden and has spent most of his life there, although his working life was spent in Hartlepool where he worked for twenty four years at SCA Boxes. Widowed in 1986, he now lives in a complex with other people where he enjoys painting, reading, music and writing. David is a Christian.

**Ann Peel** – Both of Ann Peel's grandfathers were involved in the sinking of Horden Colliery, one as a miner, the other as a blacksmith. Her father and brother were both miners. Formerly in the WRAF, Ann was also a folk singer, a telephone sales person and a proof reader. Now retired, Ann is involved in local voluntary community groups. Ensuring Horden is not forgotten is one of her main aims in life.

**Chris Robinson** - was born in Littlethorpe Maternity Hospital and spent most of her childhood in Easington Colliery. She lives with her fiancée and is currently working as a support worker for a North East-based charity. She has a passion for writing and is a keen motorcyclist who enjoys travelling.

**Susan Robinson** - Susan has lived in Easington since 1972 and comes from a long line of miners going back to the 1700s. After working for a local G.P., she trained in Alternative Therapies including Reiki and Crystal Healing. A mature student at Sunderland University, she graduated in Fine Art and has an M.A. in Women, Culture and Identity. In 2009 she completed a Certificate in Creative Writing from Lancaster University.

**Joan Wright** - A former NCB clerical worker for many years and a voluntary worker for both the Red Cross and Seaton Holme, Joan is now retired. She enjoys the popular music of her generation and also loves classical music. She wakes up with Classic FM every morning. Besides reading, she enjoys cryptic crosswords and watching old movies on the TV.

## Editors

**Wendy Robertson** is a professional writer and tutor who has written many published novels as well as regular articles and short stories. Her latest publications are the novel *The Woman Who Drew Buildings* (Headline) and a short story collection *Knives* (Iron Press). She works as a mentor and tutor for new writers.

www.wendyrobertson.com   www.roomtowrite.co.uk

**Avril Joy** was former Head of Learning and Skills at a prison for women. Now a professional writer, she has over twenty years experience in working with groups in the varying roles of teacher, facilitator and trainer. Her latest novel is *The Sweet Track* (Flambard). She has a new novel *Blood Tide* in preparation.

www.avriljoy.com